D1272283

LINEAR OPERATORS IN HILBERT SPACE

ACADEMIC PAPERBACKS*

EDITED BY Henry Booker, D. Allan Bromley, Nicholas DeClaris, W. Magnus, Alvin Nason, and A. Shenitzer

BIOLOGY

Design and Function at the Threshold of Life: The Viruses HEINZ FRAENKEL-CONRAT
The Evolution of Genetics ARNOLD W. RAVIN
Isotopes in Biology GEORGE WOLF
Life: Its Nature, Origin, and Development A. I. OPARIN
Time, Cells, and Aging BERNARD L. STREHLER

ENGINEERING

A Vector Approach to Oscillations HENRY BOOKER
Dynamic Programming and Modern Control Theory RICHARD BELLMAN and ROBERT KALABA

MATHEMATICS

Finite Permutation Groups HELMUT WIELANDT
Elements of Abstract Harmonic Analysis GEORGE BACHMAN
The Method of Averaging Functional Corrections: Theory and Applications A. YU. LUCHKA
Geometric Transformations (in two volumes) P. S. MODENOV and A. S. PARKHOMENKO
Representation Theory of Finite Groups MARTIN BURROW
Introduction to *p*-Adic Numbers and Valuation Theory GEORGE BACHMAN
Linear Operators in Hilbert Space WERNER SCHMEIDLER
Noneuclidean Geometry HERBERT MESCHKOWSKI
Quadratic Forms and Matrices N. V. YEFIMOV

PHYSICS

Crystals: Their Role in Nature and in Science CHARLES BUNN
Elementary Dynamics of Particles H. W. HARKNESS
Elementary Plane Rigid Dynamics H. W. HARKNESS
Mössbauer Effect: Principles and Applications GUNTHER K. WERTHEIM
Potential Barriers in Semiconductors B. R. GOSSICK
Principles of Vector Analysis JERRY B. MARION

*Most of these volumes are also available in a cloth bound edition.

Linear Operators in Hilbert Space

Werner Schmeidler
Technische Universität Berlin-Charlottenburg
Germany

Translation by JAY STRUM—Revised
and edited by A. SHENITZER
and D. SOLITAR
Department of Mathematics
Adelphi University
Garden City, Long Island, New York

ACADEMIC PRESS New York and London

First published in the German language under the title
Lineare Operaten im Hilbertschen Raum
and copyrighted in 1954 by B. G. Teubner Verlagsgesellshaft mbH,
Stuttgart, Germany

ACADEMIC PRESS INC.
111 Fifth Avenue, New York, New York 10003

United Kingdom Edition published by
ACADEMIC PRESS INC. (LONDON) LTD.
Berkeley Square House, London W.1

LIBRARY OF CONGRESS CATALOG CARD NUMBER : 65-19804

PRINTED IN THE UNITED STATES OF AMERICA

PREFACE

This little volume is meant as an introduction to the study of Hilbert space and its various realizations—a subject whose importance for both pure and applied mathematics is becoming more apparent all the time. To acquire a knowledge of Hilbert space is, in a sense, to take a first step in the direction of functional analysis, a subject which studies functions in general rather than specifically. The study of functions in general was advanced by the calculus of variations and above all by integral equations; it was research on integral equations that led Hilbert to the formulation of his theory of infinite dimensional space. Its subsequent generalization and abstraction, so typical of modern mathematical thought, was largely the result of demands by the physical sciences. In this book we restrict ourselves to linear problems not only because of their relative simplicity, but also because they form the only area which is by now reasonably complete; and even here we shall find it necessary to restrict ourselves to fundamentals.

Outside of a measure of mathematical maturity (which the reading of this book is supposed to promote) the prospective reader need not have special mathematical knowledge. Only the exercises and applications require knowledge of additional material, and that is always clearly described. The book is meant primarily for students of mathematics, physics, the natural sciences, and engineering and, in general, for all who wish to understand modern mathematics and its central position in the natural sciences. The purely mathematical part of the book deals with Hilbert space, linear operators, and spectral theory. The exercises and notes suggest various application of the theory. The main emphasis, however, is on a systematic development of the mathematical theory. It seems to me that this emphasis is particularly justified by the fact that in applications, of which atomic theory is the most important, the mathematical foundations are treated inadequately, and yet mathematicians and scientists experience a real need for a precise knowledge of such foundations.

The expert is not likely to find much that is new in this book. One possible exception is the note on completely continuous operators without eigenvalues; another is the proofs of the Fredholm theorems which I have not encountered in this form in the literature.

I wish to give warmest thanks to my assistant, Dr. Dietrich Morgenstern, for his devoted help and constructive criticism. I am also grateful to my colleague, Professor Dr. M. Paesler, for valuable suggestions concerning physical applications.

Berlin - Frohnau WERNER SCHMEIDLER
1954

CONTENTS

I. HILBERT SPACE

As a result of advances in mathematics the concept of space has become progressively more abstract and general. At first the term "space" signified the three-dimensional space of Euclidean geometry. Then came the discovery—in the 19th century—of non-Euclidean geometry and with it the non-Euclidean measurement of distance. This altered the concept of space without altering the name. Later it was found necessary to study n-dimensional rather than three-dimensional space. Finally Hilbert took the decisive step by investigating *infinite-dimensional space*. Our immediate concern will be with the infinite-dimensional space of sequences first studied by Hilbert.

§1. The Hilbert Space of Sequences

1. Vectors

We shall be dealing with infinite sequences $x_1, x_2, \cdots, x_n, \cdots$ of complex numbers. Sometimes we shall find it necessary to restrict ourselves to real numbers. Such exceptions will be explicitly noted.

The concepts which we are about to define are generalizations of familiar concepts in three-dimensional Euclidean space. Thus a sequence $\mathfrak{x} = (x_1, x_2, \cdots, x_n, \cdots)$ is called a point in the space $\mathfrak{H}_0$ provided its "distance" $\sqrt{\sum_{\alpha=1}^{\infty} |x_\alpha|^2}$ from the "origin" $(0, 0, \cdots, 0, \cdots)$ is finite, i.e., provided the series

$$\sum_{\alpha=1}^{\infty} | x_\alpha^2$$

converges; $\mathfrak{x}$ is referred to as a vector with components $x_1, x_2, \cdots, x_n, \cdots$ and norm

$$\|\mathfrak{x}\| = \sqrt{\sum_{\alpha=1}^{\infty} |x_\alpha|^2}.$$

We define the sum $\mathfrak{x} + \mathfrak{y}$ of the vectors $\mathfrak{x} = (x_1, x_2, \cdots)$ and $\mathfrak{y} = (y_1, y_2, \cdots)$ as the vector with components $x_1 + y_1$, $x_2 + y_2, \cdots$. To justify this definition we must show that $\mathfrak{x} + \mathfrak{y}$ is an element of $\mathfrak{H}_0$, i.e., that the series

$$\sum_{\alpha=1}^{\infty} |x_\alpha + y_\alpha|^2 = \sum_{\alpha=1}^{\infty} |x_\alpha|^2 + \sum_{\alpha=1}^{\infty} x_\alpha \bar{y}_\alpha + \sum_{\alpha=1}^{\infty} \bar{x}_\alpha y_\alpha + \sum_{\alpha=1}^{\infty} |y_\alpha|^2$$

converges. Using the triangle inequality and the Schwarz inequality we have, for each n,

$$\left|\sum_{\alpha=1}^{n} x_\alpha \bar{y}_\alpha\right| \leqq \sum_{\alpha=1}^{n} |x_\alpha|\,|y_\alpha| \leqq \sqrt{\sum_{\alpha=1}^{n} |x_\alpha|^2 \cdot \sum_{\alpha=1}^{n} |y_\alpha|^2},$$

and therefore

$$\sum_{\alpha=1}^{\infty} |x_\alpha|\,|y_\alpha| \leqq \sqrt{\sum_{\alpha=1}^{\infty} |x_\alpha|^2 \cdot \sum_{\alpha=1}^{\infty} |y_\alpha|^2}.$$

Hence the series $\sum_{\alpha=1}^{\infty} |x_\alpha|\,|y_\alpha|$ converges. This implies the convergence of $\sum_{\alpha=1}^{\infty} x_\alpha \bar{y}_\alpha$ and $\sum_{\alpha=1}^{\infty} \bar{x}_\alpha y_\alpha$ and so proves that $\mathfrak{x} + \mathfrak{y}$ is an element of $\mathfrak{H}_0$. Clearly $\mathfrak{x} + \mathfrak{y} = \mathfrak{y} + \mathfrak{x}$ and $\mathfrak{x} + (\mathfrak{y} + \mathfrak{z}) = (\mathfrak{x} + \mathfrak{y}) + \mathfrak{z}$.

If $\mathfrak{x}$ is a vector and λ a scalar we define $\lambda\mathfrak{x}$ as the vector with components $\lambda x_1, \lambda x_2, \cdots$. It is clear that $\lambda\mathfrak{x}$ belongs to $\mathfrak{H}_0$. Also, $\lambda(\mathfrak{x} + \mathfrak{y}) = (\mathfrak{x} + \mathfrak{y})\lambda = \lambda\mathfrak{x} + \lambda\mathfrak{y}$.

Using the "unit vectors"

$\mathfrak{e}_1$ with components $1, 0, 0, \cdots$
$\mathfrak{e}_2$ with components $0, 1, 0, \cdots$
....

we can express each vector $\mathfrak{x}$ in the form

$$\mathfrak{x} = x_1\mathfrak{e}_1 + x_2\mathfrak{e}_2 + \cdots.$$

This notation is self-explanatory.[1] Just as in the case of finite-dimensional spaces, we speak of a linear combination $\lambda_1\mathfrak{x}_1 + \cdots$

[1] At this stage, $x_1\mathfrak{e}_1 + x_2\mathfrak{e}_2 + \cdots$ can only be regarded as another notation for the vector $(x_1, x_2, \cdots)$. After introduction of the notion of convergence of a sequence of vectors (cf. 2. below), $x_1\mathfrak{e}_1 + x_2\mathfrak{e}_2 + \cdots$ may be interpreted as the limit of the sequence of vectors $x_1\mathfrak{e}_1$, $x_1\mathfrak{e}_1 + x_2\mathfrak{e}_2, \cdots$. (Ed.)

$+ \lambda_m \mathfrak{x}_m$ of a finite set of vectors $\mathfrak{x}_1, \cdots, \mathfrak{x}_m$ in $\mathfrak{H}_0$ and of the linear manifold spanned by a (finite or infinite) set of vectors in $\mathfrak{H}_0$. The latter is defined as the totality of (finite) linear combinations of vectors in the set.

The notion of scalar product in n-dimensional Euclidean space suggests the following definition of the scalar product $(\mathfrak{x}, \mathfrak{y})$ of two vectors $\mathfrak{x}$ and $\mathfrak{y}$ in $\mathfrak{H}_0$:

$$(\mathfrak{x}, \mathfrak{y}) = \sum_{\alpha=1}^{\infty} x_\alpha \bar{y}_\alpha = \overline{(\mathfrak{y}, \mathfrak{x})}.$$

That $(\mathfrak{x}, \mathfrak{y})$ defines a complex number follows from Schwarz's inequality. In particular,

$$(\mathfrak{x}, \mathfrak{x}) = \|\mathfrak{x}\|^2.$$

The definition of the angle φ between two vectors $\mathfrak{x} \neq 0$ and $\mathfrak{y} \neq 0$ is also patterned after n-dimensional Euclidean space:

$$\cos \varphi = \frac{(\mathfrak{x}, \mathfrak{y})}{\|\mathfrak{x}\| \cdot \|\mathfrak{y}\|}.$$

If $\mathfrak{x}$ and $\mathfrak{y}$ have real components, then $\cos \varphi$ is a real number. Otherwise $\cos \varphi$ may be a complex number. If

$$(\mathfrak{x}, \mathfrak{y}) = 0,$$

then we say that the vectors $\mathfrak{x}$ and $\mathfrak{y}$ are orthogonal. Then, clearly, $(\mathfrak{y}, \mathfrak{x})$ is also zero.

Scalar products have the following linearity properties:

$$(\lambda\mathfrak{x}, \mathfrak{y}) = \lambda(\mathfrak{x}, \mathfrak{y}),$$

$$(\mathfrak{x}, \lambda\mathfrak{y}) = \bar{\lambda}(\mathfrak{x}, \mathfrak{y}),$$

$$(\mathfrak{x}, \mathfrak{y} + \mathfrak{z}) = (\mathfrak{x}, \mathfrak{y}) + (\mathfrak{x}, \mathfrak{z}),$$

$$(\mathfrak{x} + \mathfrak{y}, \mathfrak{z}) = (\mathfrak{x}, \mathfrak{z}) + (\mathfrak{y}, \mathfrak{z}).$$

Additional basic properties of scalar products are the Schwarz inequality

$$|(\mathfrak{x}, \mathfrak{y})| \leqq \|\mathfrak{x}\| \cdot \|\mathfrak{y}\|$$

and the triangle inequality

$$\|\mathfrak{x} - \mathfrak{y}\| \leqq \|\mathfrak{x}\| + \|\mathfrak{y}\|.$$

To prove the triangle inequality note that, in view of Schwarz's inequality,

$$\|\mathfrak{x}-\mathfrak{y}\|^2 = (\mathfrak{x}-\mathfrak{y}, \mathfrak{x}) - (\mathfrak{x}-\mathfrak{y}, \mathfrak{y}) \leqq \|\mathfrak{x}-\mathfrak{y}\| \cdot \|\mathfrak{x}\| + \|\mathfrak{x}-\mathfrak{y}\| \cdot \|\mathfrak{y}\|$$
$$= \|\mathfrak{x}-\mathfrak{y}\| \cdot (\|\mathfrak{x}\| + \|\mathfrak{y}\|).$$

This implies the triangle inequality for the case $\|\mathfrak{x}-\mathfrak{y}\| \neq 0$. If $\|\mathfrak{x}-\mathfrak{y}\| = 0$, the required conclusion is trivially true.

We note that our way of "measuring distance" in $\mathfrak{H}_0$ is similar to that used in Euclidean space. In the sequel we shall have occasion to speak of more general ways of measuring distance.

2. *Strong Convergence and Completeness*

Using the above basic concepts we can now define a notion of convergence in $\mathfrak{H}_0$. We say that *a sequence of vectors* $\mathfrak{x}_1, \mathfrak{x}_2, \cdots$ *converges* (*strongly*) *to a limit* vector $\mathfrak{x}$ if for all $n > N(\delta)$ we have $\|\mathfrak{x}_n - \mathfrak{x}\| < \delta$. In symbols

$$\lim_{n\to\infty} \mathfrak{x}_n = \mathfrak{x}, \qquad \text{or simply,} \qquad \mathfrak{x}_n \to \mathfrak{x}.$$

If the sequence of vectors $\mathfrak{x}_1, \mathfrak{x}_2, \cdots$ converges to $\mathfrak{x}$, then the sequence of the αth components $x_\alpha^{(n)}$ of the $\mathfrak{x}_n$ converges in the usual sense to the αth component x_α of the limit $\mathfrak{x}$; i.e., $x_\alpha^{(n)} \to x_\alpha$ $(\alpha = 1, 2, \cdots)$. This follows from the inequality

$$|x_\alpha^{(n)} - x_\alpha| \leqq \|\mathfrak{x}_n - \mathfrak{x}\| < \delta.$$

The converse is false: If $x_\alpha^{(n)} \to x_\alpha$ $(\alpha = 1, 2, \cdots)$, then it need not follow that $\mathfrak{x}_n \to \mathfrak{x}$. To see this consider the sequence of unit vectors $\mathfrak{x}_n = \mathfrak{e}_n$; here $\lim_{n\to\infty} x_\alpha^{(n)} = 0$ $(\alpha = 1, 2, \cdots)$ but $\|\mathfrak{x}_n - 0\| = 1$ for all n.

The notion of continuity of a function is closely related to the notion of convergence. We say that a function $F(\mathfrak{x})$ is defined in some subset $\mathfrak{D}$ of $\mathfrak{H}_0$ if with every vector $\mathfrak{x}$ in $\mathfrak{D}$ there is associated a complex number $F(\mathfrak{x})$. $\mathfrak{D}$ is called the domain of definition of F. F is said to be continuous at a point $\mathfrak{x}_0$ in $\mathfrak{D}$ if for every sequence of points $\mathfrak{x}_n$ in $\mathfrak{D}$, $\mathfrak{x}_n \to \mathfrak{x}_0$ implies $F(\mathfrak{x}_n) \to$

$F(\mathfrak{x}_0)$ in the sense of ordinary convergence. This definition can be readily extended to functions of several vector variables.

We shall now show that the scalar product $(\mathfrak{x}, \mathfrak{y})$ is a continuous function of $\mathfrak{x}$ and $\mathfrak{y}$, i.e., that $\mathfrak{x}_n \to \mathfrak{x}$ and $\mathfrak{y}_n \to \mathfrak{y}$ imply that $(\mathfrak{x}_n, \mathfrak{y}_n) \to (\mathfrak{x}, \mathfrak{y})$. In fact,

$$\begin{aligned}(\mathfrak{x}_n, \mathfrak{y}_n) - (\mathfrak{x}, \mathfrak{y}) &= (\mathfrak{x}_n, \mathfrak{y}_n) - (\mathfrak{x}_n, \mathfrak{y}) + (\mathfrak{x}_n, \mathfrak{y}) - (\mathfrak{x}, \mathfrak{y}) \\ &= (\mathfrak{x}_n, \mathfrak{y}_n - \mathfrak{y}) + (\mathfrak{x}_n - \mathfrak{x}, \mathfrak{y}) \\ &= (\mathfrak{x}_n - \mathfrak{x} + \mathfrak{x}, \mathfrak{y}_n - \mathfrak{y}) + (\mathfrak{x}_n - \mathfrak{x}, \mathfrak{y}) \\ &= (\mathfrak{x}_n - \mathfrak{x}, \mathfrak{y}_n - \mathfrak{y}) + (\mathfrak{x}, \mathfrak{y}_n - \mathfrak{y}) + (\mathfrak{x}_n - \mathfrak{x}, \mathfrak{y}).\end{aligned}$$

In view of the triangle inequality (for complex numbers),

$$\begin{aligned}|(\mathfrak{x}_n, \mathfrak{y}_n) - (\mathfrak{x}, \mathfrak{y})| \leqq |(\mathfrak{x}_n - \mathfrak{x}, \mathfrak{y}_n - \mathfrak{y})| + |(\mathfrak{x}, \mathfrak{y}_n - \mathfrak{y})| \\ + |(\mathfrak{x}_n - \mathfrak{x}, \mathfrak{y})|;\end{aligned}$$

hence by the Schwarz inequality,

$$\begin{aligned}|(\mathfrak{x}_n, \mathfrak{y}_n) - \mathfrak{x}), \mathfrak{y})| \leqq \|\mathfrak{x}_n - \mathfrak{x}\| \cdot \|\mathfrak{y}_n - \mathfrak{y}\| + \|\mathfrak{x}\| \cdot \|\mathfrak{y}_n - \mathfrak{y}\| \\ + \|\mathfrak{x}_n - \mathfrak{x}\| \cdot \|\mathfrak{y}\|.\end{aligned}$$

The expression on the right becomes arbitrarily small for n sufficiently large. But this means that $(\mathfrak{x}_n, \mathfrak{y}_n) \to (\mathfrak{x}, \mathfrak{y})$, which is what we wished to prove. In particular, $\mathfrak{x}_n \to \mathfrak{x}$ implies $\|\mathfrak{x}_n\| \to \|\mathfrak{x}\|$, which proves continuity of the norm.

We shall now prove a fundamental property of the space $\mathfrak{H}_0$, namely, its completeness. Note that $\mathfrak{x}_n \to \mathfrak{x}$ implies $\|\mathfrak{x}_n - \mathfrak{x}_m\| < \delta$ for all sufficiently large n and m. We propose to show that, conversely, $\|\mathfrak{x}_n - \mathfrak{x}_m\| < \delta$ for all sufficiently large n and m implies the existence of a vector $\mathfrak{x}$ such that $\mathfrak{x}_n \to \mathfrak{x}$, which is what we mean by the completeness of $\mathfrak{H}_0$. A sequence $\mathfrak{x}_n$ for which $\|\mathfrak{x}_n - \mathfrak{x}_m\| < \delta$ for all sufficiently large n and m is called a Cauchy sequence. Hence what we are about to prove is that every Cauchy sequence in $\mathfrak{H}_0$ converges (to a limit in $\mathfrak{H}_0$).

Observe that if $\mathfrak{e}_r$ is the rth unit vector, then the sequence of complex numbers $(\mathfrak{x}_n, \mathfrak{e}_r)$ is a Cauchy sequence. Indeed,

$$|(\mathfrak{x}_n, \mathfrak{e}_r) - (\mathfrak{x}_m, \mathfrak{e}_r)| = |(\mathfrak{x}_n - \mathfrak{x}_m, \mathfrak{e}_r)| \leqq \|\mathfrak{x}_n - \mathfrak{x}_m\| < \delta$$

for all sufficiently large n and m. In view of the completeness of the system of complex numbers we may conclude the existence of $\lim_{n\to\infty} (\mathfrak{x}_n, \mathfrak{e}_r) = x_r$ for $r = 1, 2, \cdots$.

We now show that $\sum_{r=1}^{\infty} |x_r|^2$ converges, i.e., that $\mathfrak{x} = (x_1, x_2, \cdots)$ is a vector in $\mathfrak{H}_0$. To this end we note first that the sequence $\mathfrak{x}_n$ is bounded, i.e., that the norms $\|\mathfrak{x}_n\|$ have a common upper bound. This follows from the fact that for a fixed m and all sufficiently large n, $\|\mathfrak{x}_n\| = \|\mathfrak{x}_m - (\mathfrak{x}_m - \mathfrak{x}_n)\| \leqq \|\mathfrak{x}_m\| + \|\mathfrak{x}_m - \mathfrak{x}_n\| \leqq \|\mathfrak{x}_m\| + \delta$. If we apply the boundedness of the $\|\mathfrak{x}_n\|$ to the inequality

$$|(\mathfrak{x}_n, \mathfrak{x}_n) - (\mathfrak{x}_m, \mathfrak{x}_m)| = |(\mathfrak{x}_n, \mathfrak{x}_n - \mathfrak{x}_m) + (\mathfrak{x}_n - \mathfrak{x}_m, \mathfrak{x}_m)|$$
$$\leqq (\|\mathfrak{x}_n\| + \|\mathfrak{x}_m\|) \cdot \|\mathfrak{x}_n - \mathfrak{x}_m\|,$$

we can conclude that the sequence $(\mathfrak{x}_n, \mathfrak{x}_n) = \|\mathfrak{x}_n\|^2$ is a Cauchy sequence of nonnegative real numbers. As such it must converge to some real limit $q \geqq 0$. Put $\mathfrak{x}_n = \sum_{r=1}^{\infty} x_r^{(n)} \mathfrak{e}_r$. We have

$$q - \sum_{r=1}^{k} |x_r|^2 = q - \lim_{n\to\infty} \sum_{r=1}^{k} (|\mathfrak{x}_n, \mathfrak{e}_r)|^2 = q - \lim_{n\to\infty} \sum_{r=1}^{k} |x_r^{(n)}|^2$$
$$= \lim_{n\to\infty} \sum_{r=1}^{\infty} |x_r^{(n)}|^2 - \lim_{n\to\infty} \sum_{r=1}^{k} |x_r^{(n)}|^2$$
$$= \lim_{n\to\infty} \sum_{r=k+1}^{\infty} |x_r^{(n)}|^2 \geqq 0,$$

which means that $\sum_{r=1}^{k} |x_r|^2 \leqq q$. But this implies the convergence of $\sum_{r=1}^{\infty} |x_r|^2$ and proves that $\mathfrak{x} = (x_1, x_2, \cdots)$ is an element of $\mathfrak{H}_0$.

To complete the proof (of the completeness of $\mathfrak{H}_0$) we now show that our Cauchy sequence $\mathfrak{x}_n$ converges to the limit $\mathfrak{x}$. Observe that $\|\mathfrak{x}_n - \mathfrak{x}_m\| < \sqrt{\delta}$ for all sufficiently large n and m and for every value of k we have

$$\sum_{\alpha=1}^{k} |x_\alpha^{(n)} - x_\alpha^{(m)}|^2 < \delta.$$

Letting $m \to \infty$ in the last inequality and bearing in mind that $x_\alpha^{(m)} \to x_\alpha$ we see that

$$\sum_{\alpha=1}^{k} |x_\alpha^{(n)} - x_\alpha|^2 \leqq \delta, \qquad \text{i.e.} \qquad \sum_{\alpha=1}^{\infty} |x_\alpha^{(n)} - x_\alpha|^2 \leqq \delta.$$

Since $\sum_{\alpha=1}^{\infty} |x_\alpha^{(n)} - x_\alpha|^2 = \|\mathfrak{x}_n - \mathfrak{x}\|^2 \leqq \delta$, we conclude that $\mathfrak{x}_n \to \mathfrak{x}$. This completes the proof of the completeness of $\mathfrak{H}_0$.

3. Weak Convergence

In addition to strong convergence it is natural to consider another notion of convergence whose essential feature is componentwise convergence. We say that a sequence $\mathfrak{x}_n$ converges weakly to $\mathfrak{x}$—in symbols, $\mathfrak{x}_n \rightharpoonup \mathfrak{x}$—whenever, in addition to the convergence of the series $\sum_{\alpha=1}^{\infty} |x_\alpha^{(n)}|^2 = \|\mathfrak{x}_n\|^2$ for $n = 1, 2, 3, \cdots$ and of the series $\sum_{\alpha=1}^{\infty} |x_\alpha|^2 = \|\mathfrak{x}\|^2$, we have

(a) $\lim_{n\to\infty} x_\alpha^{(n)} = x_\alpha \qquad (\alpha = 1, 2, \cdots)$

(componentwise convergence),

(b) $\|\mathfrak{x}_n\|^2 = \sum_{\alpha=1}^{\infty} |x_\alpha^{(n)}|^2 < C$ for all n

(uniform boundedness of norms).[2]

We have already shown that strong convergence implies componentwise convergence and uniform boundedness of the norms, i.e., strong convergence implies weak convergence. The converse is false, for the sequence of unit vectors converges to zero in the sense of weak convergence but not in the sense of strong convergence. We shall now establish a new characterization of weak convergence.

Our first result: *For any weakly convergent sequence* $\mathfrak{x}_n \rightharpoonup \mathfrak{x}$ *and any* $\mathfrak{y}$ *in* $\mathfrak{H}_0$ *we have* $(\mathfrak{x}_n, \mathfrak{y}) \to (\mathfrak{x}, \mathfrak{y})$.

For proof, note that

$$\sum_{\alpha=1}^{\infty} x_\alpha^{(n)}\bar{y}_\alpha - \sum_{\alpha=1}^{\infty} x_\alpha\bar{y}_\alpha = \sum_{\alpha=1}^{\infty} (x_\alpha^{(n)} - x_\alpha)\bar{y}_\alpha$$

$$= \sum_{\alpha=1}^{m} (x_\alpha^{(n)} - x_\alpha)\bar{y}_\alpha + \sum_{\alpha=m+1}^{\infty} (x_\alpha^{(n)} - x_\alpha)\bar{y}_\alpha.$$

[2] Note that if $\mathfrak{x}_1, \mathfrak{x}_2, \cdots$ satisfy (a) and (b), then $(x_1, x_2, \cdots)$ is in $\mathfrak{H}_0$. In fact, $|x_1|^2 + \cdots + |x_i|^2 = \lim_{n\to\infty}|x_1^{(n)}|^2 + \cdots + \lim_{n\to\infty}|x_i^{(n)}|^2 = \lim_{n\to\infty} (|x_1^{(n)}|^2 + \cdots + |x_i^{(n)}|^2)$. But $(|x_1^{(n)}|^2 + \cdots + |x_i^{(n)}|^2) \leqq \|\mathfrak{x}_n\|^2 < C$ for every n. Hence $|x_1|^2 + \cdots + |x_i|^2 \leqq C$ for every i, which implies that $(x_1, x_2, \cdots)$ is an element of $\mathfrak{H}_0$, as asserted. (Ed.)

If we fix m, then the first summand above tends to zero as $n \to \infty$. The second summand is in absolute value at most equal to

$$\sqrt{\sum_{\alpha=m+1}^{\infty} |x_\alpha^{(n)} - x_\alpha|^2 \cdot \sum_{\alpha=m+1}^{\infty} |y_\alpha|^2}.$$

The second factor under this last radical becomes arbitrarily small as $m \to \infty$ while, by the triangle inequality, the first factor is at most equal to $\|\mathfrak{x}_n\| + \|\mathfrak{x}\|$, i.e., is bounded for all n. But this means that $\sum_{\alpha=1}^{\infty} (x_\alpha^{(n)} - x_\alpha)\bar{y}_\alpha \to 0$ as $n \to \infty$, and our result follows. Conversely, *given a sequence* $\mathfrak{x}_n$ *such that for all* $\mathfrak{y}$ *in* $\mathfrak{H}_0$ $(\mathfrak{x}_n, \mathfrak{y}) \to (\mathfrak{x}, \mathfrak{y})$ *it follows that* $\mathfrak{x}_n \rightharpoonup \mathfrak{x}$. Indeed, if we put $(\mathfrak{x}_n, \mathfrak{e}_r) = x_r^{(n)}$, $(\mathfrak{x}, \mathfrak{e}_r) = x_r$ and $\mathfrak{y} = \mathfrak{e}_r$, we see that $x_r^{(n)} \to x_r$. It remains to prove the uniform boundedness of the $\|\mathfrak{x}_n\|$. This we do next.

Note that for any $\mathfrak{y}$ the scalar product $(\mathfrak{x}_n, \mathfrak{y})$ is in absolute value uniformly bounded for all n. We shall use this fact to prove more than is required: namely, we shall show that there exists a constant C such that for all $\mathfrak{y}$ in $\mathfrak{H}_0$

$$|(\mathfrak{x}_n, \mathfrak{y})| \leqq C\|\mathfrak{y}\|.$$

In order to prove this "global" result we first prove the "local" boundedness result: $|(\mathfrak{x}_n, \mathfrak{y})| \leqq C$ for all $\mathfrak{y}$ in a closed δ neighborhood of some vector $\mathfrak{z}_0$, i.e., for all $\mathfrak{y}$ such that $\|\mathfrak{y} - \mathfrak{z}_0\| \leqq \delta$.

If this local contention were false, then given a neighborhood U_0 of a point $\mathfrak{z}_0$ and a number c_1 we could assert the existence of a point $\mathfrak{z}_1$, *interior to* U_0 and a point $\mathfrak{x}_{n_1}$ such that $|(\mathfrak{x}_{n_1}, \mathfrak{z}_1)| > c_1$. In view of the continuity of the inner product we could make the stronger assertion that $|(\mathfrak{x}_{n_1}, \mathfrak{y})| > c_1$ for all $\mathfrak{y}$ in a sufficiently small neighborhood U_1 of $\mathfrak{z}_1$ with $U_1 \subset U_0$. Similarly, given a number c_2 we could assert the existence of a neighborhood U_2 interior to U_1 and a point $\mathfrak{x}_{n_2}$ such that $|(\mathfrak{x}_{n_2}, \mathfrak{y})| > c_2$ for $\mathfrak{y}$ in U_2.

Repeated use of this argument enables us to assert the existence of a nested sequence of neighborhoods $U_0 \supset U_1 \supset \cdots$ with radii going to zero such that $|(\mathfrak{x}_{n_j}, \mathfrak{y})| > c_j = j$ for $\mathfrak{y}$ in $U_j \, (j = 1, 2, \cdots)$. The centers of the U_j form a Cauchy sequence and, since $\mathfrak{H}_0$ is complete, this sequence converges to a limit vector $\mathfrak{y}^*$ contained in all the U_j and satisfying the inequalities

$$|(\mathfrak{x}_{n_1}, \mathfrak{y}^*)| > 1, \quad |(\mathfrak{x}_{n_2}, \mathfrak{y}^*)| > 2, \cdots .$$

But this contradicts the uniform boundedness of the $|(\mathfrak{x}_n, \mathfrak{y}^*)|$.

Now that our "local" contention is established the proof of the "global" result is easy. Indeed, if $\mathfrak{y} \neq 0$, then

$$(\mathfrak{x}_n, \mathfrak{y}) = \frac{\|\mathfrak{y}\|}{\delta}\left(\mathfrak{x}_n, \frac{\mathfrak{y}}{\|\mathfrak{y}\|}\delta + \mathfrak{z}_0\right) - \frac{\|\mathfrak{y}\|}{\delta}(\mathfrak{x}_n, \mathfrak{z}_0).$$

Note that $(\mathfrak{y}/\|\mathfrak{y}\|)\delta + \mathfrak{z}_0$ differs from $\mathfrak{z}_0$ by a vector whose norm does not exceed δ. Hence, in view of our "local" result, $|(\mathfrak{x}_n, (\mathfrak{y}/\|\mathfrak{y}\|)\delta + \mathfrak{z}_0)| \leqq C$ and $|(\mathfrak{x}_n, \mathfrak{z}_0)| \leqq C$ for all n. This implies that

$$|(\mathfrak{x}_n, \mathfrak{y})| < \frac{2C}{\delta}\|\mathfrak{y}\|$$

for arbitrary $\mathfrak{y} \neq 0$ and proves our "global" result. In particular, if we put $\mathfrak{y} = \mathfrak{x}_n$, then

$$(\mathfrak{x}_n, \mathfrak{x}_n) < \frac{2C}{\delta}\|\mathfrak{x}_n\|, \qquad \|\mathfrak{x}_n\| < \frac{2C}{\delta},$$

which proves that *the norms of the vectors of a weakly convergent sequence are uniformly bounded.*

All in all, *a sequence $\mathfrak{x}_1, \mathfrak{x}_2, \cdots$ converges weakly to a limit $\mathfrak{x}$ if and only if for all $\mathfrak{y}$ in $\mathfrak{H}_0$*

$$(\mathfrak{x}_n, \mathfrak{y}) \to (\mathfrak{x}, \mathfrak{y}) \qquad \text{as} \quad n \to \infty.$$

In the sequel we shall obtain necessary and sufficient conditions for weak convergence of a sequence which involve only the elements of the sequence in question.

§2. Abstract Hilbert Space

1. The Axioms of Hilbert Space

Modern mathematics owes much of its success to the art of isolating and formulating abstractly the essence of a concept or a proof. We shall employ this method to characterize Hilbert space axiomatically.

From now on we should not think of the elements of the abstract Hilbert space $\mathfrak{H}$ as being concrete objects such as points or vectors, but rather as entities obeying the rules of Hilbert space as defined below.

A Hilbert space $\mathfrak{H}$ is a system of elements $f, g, h, \cdots$ satisfying the following postulates:

(a) *$\mathfrak{H}$ is a linear (or vector) space.* This means that two operations are defined in $\mathfrak{H}$, an addition between elements of $\mathfrak{H}$ and a multiplication of elements of $\mathfrak{H}$ by scalars (complex numbers) $\lambda, \mu, \rho, \cdots$ such that the following rules hold:

$$f + g = g + f, \qquad f + (g + h) = (f + g) + h,$$

$$\lambda(f + g) = \lambda f + \lambda g, \qquad (\lambda + \mu)f = \lambda f + \mu f,$$

$$(\lambda\mu)f = \lambda(\mu f), \qquad 1 \cdot f = f.$$[3]

(b) *A distance function is defined in $\mathfrak{H}$ by means of a scalar product.*

The scalar product of two elements f and g in $\mathfrak{H}$ is a complex number denoted by (f, g). We require that it have the following properties:

$$(\lambda f, g) = \lambda(f, g); (g, f) = \overline{(f, g)}; (f_1 + f_2, g) = (f_1, g) + (f_2, g);$$

$(f, f) > 0$ except when $f = 0$, in which case $(f, g) = 0$ for all g and, in particular, $(f, f) = 0$.

These axioms imply that

$$(f, g_1 + g_2) = \overline{(g_1 + g_2, f)} = \overline{(g_1, f)} + \overline{(g_2, f)} = (f, g_1) + (f, g_2),$$

$$(f, \lambda g) = \bar{\lambda}(f, g).$$

We call $\sqrt{(f, f)} = \|f\|$ the norm of f. Elements whose norm is one are said to be normalized. The Schwarz inequality

$$|(f, g)| \leqq \|f\| \cdot \|g\|$$

[3] These axioms do not provide for a zero vector. To fill the gap we require that $0 \cdot f = 0 \cdot g$ for all f and g in $\mathfrak{H}$ and call $0 \cdot f$ the zero vector. The symbol for the zero vector is 0. Now the vectors form a group under addition. (Ed.)

is a consequence of our axioms. It certainly holds for $g = 0$. If $g \neq 0$, then

$$0 \leqq (f + \lambda g, f + \lambda g) = (f, f) + \lambda(g, f) + \bar{\lambda}(f, g) + |\lambda|^2(g, g).$$

If we put $\lambda = -(f, g)/(g, g)$, in the above equality, we get

$$(f, f) - \frac{(f, g)(g, f)}{(g, g)} - \frac{(g, f)(f, g)}{(g, g)} + \frac{(f, g)(g, f)}{(g, g)} \geqq 0,$$

i.e.,

$$(f, f)(g, g) \geqq (f, g)(g, f) = |(f, g)|^2,$$

which proves our contention.

We now define the distance between two elements f and g by means of the notion of norm: distance between f and $g = \|f - g\|$. We again have the triangle inequality:

$$\|f - g\| \leqq \|f\| + \|g\|.$$

The proof of this inequality runs exactly as in $\mathfrak{H}_0$ and need not be repeated.

Using the notion of distance we can now define strong convergence in abstract Hilbert space:

A sequence $f_1, f_2, \cdots$ of elements of $\mathfrak{H}$ is said to be strongly convergent to a limit f if $\|f_n - f\| \to 0$ as $n \to \infty$. Every strongly convergent sequence is a Cauchy sequence, i.e., $\|f_n - f_m\| \to 0$ as $n \to \infty$, $m \to \infty$. In order for the converse theorem to hold we require that $\mathfrak{H}$ satisfy the following axiom:

(c) *$\mathfrak{H}$ is complete, i.e., every Cauchy sequence in $\mathfrak{H}$ must converge to a limit in $\mathfrak{H}$.*

In view of our findings concerning weak convergence in $\mathfrak{H}_0$ it is natural to define weak convergence in $\mathfrak{H}$ as follows:

A sequence $f_1, f_2, \cdots$ of elements of $\mathfrak{H}$ is said to be weakly convergent to an element f in $\mathfrak{H}$ if

$$\lim_{n \to \infty} (f_n, g) = (f, g)$$

for every element g in $\mathfrak{H}$.

One can easily show that every strongly convergent sequence is also weakly convergent. The converse is false, as we shall show in §3.

The existence of the space $\mathfrak{H}_0$ guarantees that the axioms (a), (b), (c) for abstract Hilbert space are consistent. Another realization of abstract Hilbert space is furnished by the n-dimensional Euclidean space of points $(x_1, \cdots, x_n)$. If we wish to characterize infinite-dimensional abstract Hilbert space $\mathfrak{H}$ we shall therefore have to postulate something about the dimension of $\mathfrak{H}$. We want this dimension to be denumerably infinite—but first we must define what we mean by the dimension of an abstract space.

Consider a subset $\mathfrak{T}$ of $\mathfrak{H}$. We say that $\mathfrak{T}$ is "dense in $\mathfrak{H}$" if every neighborhood of any point in $\mathfrak{H}$ always contains an element of $\mathfrak{T}$. This condition means that, given an arbitrary $\delta > 0$ and an arbitrary f in $\mathfrak{H}$, we can always find a g in $\mathfrak{T}$ such that $\|f - g\| < \delta$. We shall say that $\mathfrak{T}$ is a fundamental set in $\mathfrak{H}$ if the totality of all finite linear combinations $\sum_{\alpha=1}^{\infty} c_\alpha f_\alpha$, where the f_α belong to $\mathfrak{T}$, forms a dense set in $\mathfrak{H}$. We can now make the following definition: The smallest possible cardinality of a fundamental set in $\mathfrak{H}$ is said to be the dimension of $\mathfrak{H}$. We require $\mathfrak{H}$ to satisfy the following additional postulate:

(d) *The dimension of $\mathfrak{H}$ is denumerably infinite.* This means that $\mathfrak{H}$ contains a denumerable fundamental set but not a finite one.

The above four properties characterize abstract Hilbert space. This assertion will be discussed and proved in 4. of §3.

2. *The Space of Square-Integrable Functions*

Besides $\mathfrak{H}_0$, another important realization of $\mathfrak{H}$ is the space $\mathfrak{L}_2(a, b)$ consisting of all complex-valued square-integrable (in the sense of Lebesgue) functions $f(t)$ defined over the real interval $a \leqq t \leqq b$, with an appropriate notion of scalar product. This means that $\int_a^b |f(t)|^2 \, dt$ and $\int_\alpha^\beta f(t) \, dt$, where $a \leqq \alpha \leqq \beta \leqq b$, must both exist. Here a and b can be $\mp\infty$ but α and β must be finite. As is well known, two such functions are considered essentially the same if the set of points at which they differ is of measure zero. In order to show that $\mathfrak{L}_2(a, b)$ is a Hilbert space we must show that it satisfies axioms (a) through (d). That axiom (a) holds in $\mathfrak{L}_2(a, b)$ follows from well-known properties of $\mathfrak{L}_2$-integrable functions. Axiom (b) is satisfied if we define the scalar product by

$$(f, g) = \int_a^b f(t)\overline{g(t)}\, dt.$$

Then

$$\|f\|^2 = (f, f) = \int_a^b |f(t)|^2\, dt > 0$$

for all $f \neq 0$. If $f = 0$, then $\|f\| = 0$. To show that axiom (c) holds in $\mathfrak{L}_2(a, b)$ we would have to show that any sequence $f_1(t), f_2(t), \cdots$ such that

$$\int_a^b |f_m(t) - f_n(t)|^2\, dt \to 0 \qquad \text{for} \quad n, m \to \infty$$

converges to a limit function $f(t)$ in $\mathfrak{L}_2(a, b)$. This assertion is a theorem in the theory of the Lebesgue integral, the proof of which we shall not give here as it would take us too far afield.[4] As for axiom (d), we can verify it easily by finding a complete family of orthogonal functions defined over the interval (a, b). Specifically, if a and b are both finite we can use the appropriate trigonometric functions; if either a or b is infinite, we can use the Laguerre functions; while if both a and b are infinite we can use the Hermite functions. We cannot here enter into the details of these families of functions,[5] although we shall soon examine in some detail the general concept of an orthogonal system in $\mathfrak{H}$.

§3. Orthonormal Systems of Vectors in $\mathfrak{H}$

A set (φ) of elements φ in $\mathfrak{H}$ such that each φ is normalized and any two distinct φ's are orthogonal is said to form an orthornormal system in $\mathfrak{H}$. If we do not impose the normalization condition, then we speak of an orthogonal family of

[4] See, for example, Natanson, I. P., "The Theory of Functions of a Real Variable." F. Ungar, New York, 1955 (Vol. I); 1960 (Vol. 2).

[5] See, for example, Jackson, D., "Fourier Series and Orthogonal Polynomials." The Mathematical Association of America, New York, 1941.

functions. In what follows we shall always assume—for the sake of simplicity—that our orthogonal systems of functions are normalized. This is no restriction of generality since we can always replace a (nonzero) vector φ by the normalized vector $\varphi/\|\varphi\|$. For the time being we leave open the question of cardinality of an orthonormal system of functions; later we shall show that such a system is finite or at most denumerably infinite.

1. Orthogonalization

A sequence $f_1, f_2, \cdots$ of elements in $\mathfrak{H}$ can always be made into an orthonormal (finite or infinite) sequence by a technique known as the Schmidt orthogonalization procedure. In this procedure we first delete from $f_1, f_2, \cdots$ any element which is linearly dependent on its predecessors. The result is a finite or infinite sequence which we shall again denote—for reasons of simplicity—by $f_1, f_2, \cdots$. Clearly, none of our vectors is the zero vector. We put

$$\varphi_1 = \frac{f_1}{\|f_1\|}.$$

Next we put

$$\varphi_2 = c_1\varphi_1 + c_2 f_2$$

and require that

$$(\varphi_2, \varphi_1) = c_1 + c_2(f_2, \varphi_1) = 0.$$

Then

$$\varphi_2 = c_2(f_2 - (f_2, \varphi_1)\varphi_1).$$

To normalize φ_2 we must choose $c_2 = 1/(\|f_2 - (f_2, \varphi_1)\varphi_1\|)$. That $\|f_2 - (f_2, \varphi_1)\varphi_1\| \neq 0$ follows from the linear independence of f_2 and φ_1. In general, if $\varphi_1, \cdots, \varphi_{\nu-1}$ are normalized and pairwise orthogonal vectors, we choose

$$\varphi_\nu = \frac{f_\nu - \sum_{\alpha=1}^{\nu-1} (f_\nu, \varphi_\alpha)\varphi_\alpha}{\|f_\nu - \sum_{\alpha=1}^{\nu-1} (f_\nu, \varphi_\alpha)\varphi_\alpha\|} \qquad (\nu = 2, 3, \cdots).$$

This definition is admissible; indeed, the denominator in the expression for φ_ν can never equal zero because of the linear independence of $f_\nu, \varphi_1, \cdots, \varphi_{\nu-1}$. Clearly, $(\varphi_\nu, \varphi_\alpha) = 0$ for $\alpha = 1, \cdots, \nu - 1$ and $(\varphi_\nu, \varphi_\nu) = 1$. Thus the Schmidt procedure enables us to orthonormalize a sequence, as asserted.

The coefficients (f, φ_α) in the above construction can be formed for each f in $\mathfrak{H}$. They are known as *the Fourier coefficients of f with respect to the system* (φ) and they play a fundamental role in our theory. They can be formed for any f with respect to any system (φ).

2. *Denumerability of Orthonormal Systems*

We shall now prove that any orthonormal family (φ) contains at most a countable infinity of elements. To this end we consider in $\mathfrak{H}$ an arbitrary, necessarily denumerable, fundamental set $\mathfrak{G}$. Axiom (d) guarantees the existence of such a set. Let us form the set $\mathfrak{G}'$ of all finite linear combinations of elements of $\mathfrak{G}$ with rational complex numbers as multipliers. As the union of a denumerable infinity of denumerable sets, $\mathfrak{G}'$ must be denumerable. Since $\mathfrak{G}$ is a fundamental set, every element f in $\mathfrak{H}$ can be approximated by a linear combination g^* of elements of $\mathfrak{G}$ so that $\|f - g^*\| < \delta/2$. The coefficients of g^* are complex and finite in number. They themselves can be approximated to any desired degree of accuracy by rational complex coefficients. This means that we can find a g in $\mathfrak{G}'$ such that $\|g^* - g\| < \delta/2$. But then $\|f - g\| < \delta$. Here δ can be arbitrarily small. These findings, applied to the elements φ, $\psi, \cdots$ of (φ), guarantee the existence of elements $g, h, \cdots$ in $\mathfrak{G}'$ such that

$$\|\varphi - g\| < \frac{\sqrt{2}}{2}, \quad \|\psi - h\| < \frac{\sqrt{2}}{2}, \cdots .$$

If φ and ψ are distinct, then the g and h which approximate them must also be distinct. For if $g = h$, then

$$\|\varphi - \psi\| = \|\varphi - g - (\psi - h)\| \leqq \|\varphi - g\| + \|\psi - h\| < \sqrt{2},$$

whereas we know that

$$\|\varphi - \psi\|^2 = \|\varphi\|^2 + \|\psi\|^2 = 2.$$

The cardinality of $\mathfrak{G}'$ is therefore greater than or equal to that of $\mathfrak{G}$. But since $\mathfrak{G}'$ is denumerable, (φ) can be at most denumerable, which proves that (φ) contains at most a denumerable infinity of elements.

3. *Complete and Incomplete Orthonormal Systems*

We shall need the following:

Lemma. *If an element f in $\mathfrak{H}$ is orthogonal to each of the elements $f_1, f_2, \cdots$ of a fundamental set, then $f = 0$.*

Indeed, by hypothesis, we can approximate f by a linear combination $\sum_{\alpha=1}^{m} c_\alpha f_\alpha$ of the f_α such that $\|f - \sum_{\alpha=1}^{m} c_\alpha f_\alpha\| < \delta$, whence, by Schwarz's inequality,

$$\left|\left(f, f - \sum_{\alpha=1}^{m} c_\alpha f_\alpha\right)\right| \leqq \|f\| \cdot \delta.$$

On the other hand, the left side of the above inequality is equal to $\|f\|^2$ (because $(f, f_\alpha) = 0$). Hence $\|f\| \leqq \delta$ for any δ, which implies that $\|f\| = 0$. Hence $f = 0$, as asserted.

Let us now consider an arbitrary orthonormal family (φ) in $\mathfrak{H}$. Since (φ) is at most denumerable, we can designate its elements as $\varphi_1, \varphi_2, \cdots$. For an arbitrary f in $\mathfrak{H}$ we can form the Fourier coefficients (f, φ_α). Let $f_m = \sum_{\alpha=1}^{m} (f, \varphi_\alpha)\varphi_\alpha$. Then

$$\begin{aligned} \|f - f_m\|^2 &= (f, f) - \sum_{\alpha=1}^{m} (f, \varphi_\alpha)(\varphi_\alpha, f) - \left(f, \sum_{\alpha=1}^{m} (f, \varphi_\alpha)\varphi_\alpha\right) \\ &\quad + \left(\sum_{\alpha=1}^{m} (f, \varphi_\alpha)\varphi_\alpha, \sum_{\alpha=1}^{m} (f, \varphi_\alpha)\varphi_\alpha\right) \\ &= \|f\|^2 - \sum_{\alpha=1}^{m} |(f, \varphi_\alpha)|^2 \geqq 0. \end{aligned}$$

Consequently, for any $m > 0$,

$$\sum_{\alpha=1}^{m} |(f, \varphi_\alpha)|^2 \leqq \|f\|^2.$$

This last relation is known as Bessel's inequality. If the family (φ) is infinite, we can let $m \to \infty$, obtaining in the limit the following form of Bessel's inequality:

$$\sum_{\alpha=1}^{\infty} |(f, \varphi_\alpha)|^2 \leqq \|f\|^2.$$

Moreover, if $m > n$, we see that

$$\|f_m - f_n\|^2 = \left\| \sum_{\alpha=n+1}^{m} (f, \varphi_\alpha)\varphi_\alpha \right\|^2 = \sum_{\alpha=n+1}^{m} |(f, \varphi_\alpha)|^2 < \delta,$$

for n sufficiently large. This shows that the sequence $f_1, f_2, \cdots$ is a Cauchy sequence. Since the Hilbert space $\mathfrak{H}$ is complete, there exists an element g in $\mathfrak{H}$ such that $\|g - f_m\| \to 0$ as $m \to \infty$, i.e., $f_m \to g$. We can express this fact by means of the notation

$$g = \sum_{\alpha=1}^{\infty} (f, \varphi_\alpha)\varphi_\alpha$$

and we point out that the order of the summands can be arbitrary.

Let us now examine the particular case when (φ) is a fundamental set. Then there exists a linear combination $\sum_{\alpha=1}^{m} c_\alpha \varphi_\alpha$ such that

$$\left\| f - \sum_{\alpha=1}^{m} c_\alpha \varphi_\alpha \right\| < \delta.$$

This implies

$$\left\| f - \sum_{\alpha=1}^{m} c_\alpha \varphi_\alpha \right\|^2 = \|f\|^2 - \sum_{\alpha=1}^{m} \overline{c_\alpha}(f, \varphi_\alpha) - \sum_{\alpha=1}^{m} c_\alpha \overline{(f, \varphi_\alpha)} + \sum_{\alpha=1}^{m} |c_\alpha|^2.$$

On the other hand, in deriving the Bessel inequality we saw that

$$\left\| f - \sum_{\alpha=1}^{m} (f, \varphi_\alpha)\varphi_\alpha \right\|^2 = \|f\|^2 - \sum_{\alpha=1}^{m} |(f, \varphi_\alpha)|^2.$$

Hence

$$\left\| f - \sum_{\alpha=1}^{m} c_\alpha \varphi_\alpha \right\|^2 - \left\| f - \sum_{\alpha=1}^{m} (f, \varphi_\alpha)\varphi_\alpha \right\|^2$$

$$= \sum_{\alpha=1}^{m} \{|(f, \varphi_\alpha)|^2 - \overline{c_\alpha}(f, \varphi_\alpha) - c_\alpha \overline{(f, \varphi_\alpha)} + |c_\alpha|^2\}$$

$$= \sum_{\alpha=1}^{m} |(f, \varphi_\alpha) - c_\alpha|^2 \geqq 0,$$

and therefore

$$\left\| f - \sum_{\alpha=1}^{m} (f, \varphi_\alpha)\varphi_\alpha \right\| \leqq \left\| f - \sum_{\alpha=1}^{m} c_\alpha \varphi_\alpha \right\| < \delta.$$

In our agreed-upon notation this means that

$$f = \sum_{\alpha=1}^{\infty} (f, \varphi_\alpha)\varphi_\alpha = g.$$

Thus *if* (φ) *is a fundamental set, then every element* f *in* $\mathfrak{H}$ *can be written as a series in the elements* φ_α *of* (φ) *whose coefficients are the Fourier coefficients* (f, φ_α) *of* f *with respect to* (φ). In this case (φ) is called a *complete orthonormal system.*

We shall now prove that for complete orthonormal systems the Bessel inequality becomes an equality,

$$\sum_{\alpha=1}^{\infty} |(f, \varphi_\alpha)|^2 = \|f\|^2$$

(known as *the completeness relation*).

We recall the equality

$$\left\| f - \sum_{\alpha=1}^{m} (f, \varphi_\alpha)\varphi_\alpha \right\|^2 = \|f\|^2 - \sum_{\alpha=1}^{m} |(f, \varphi_\alpha)|^2.$$

We have just shown that the left side of this equality is $< \delta^2$ for sufficiently large m. Hence as $m \to \infty$ we obtain the required equality.

Conversely, if for every f in $\mathfrak{H}$ the Bessel inequality holds with the equality sign, i.e., if the completeness equality holds for all f in $\mathfrak{H}$, then the system (φ) must be a complete orthonormal system. For we can associate with any f the element $f_m = \sum_{\alpha=1}^{m} (f, \varphi_\alpha)\varphi_\alpha$ and

$$\|f - f_m\|^2 = \|f\|^2 - \sum_{\alpha=1}^{m} |(f, \varphi_\alpha)|^2 < \delta^2.$$

Thus f can be approximated by f_m to any desired degree of accuracy, which means that (φ) is a fundamental set. Hence *the completeness relation characterizes complete orthonormal families.*

Let us now assume that (φ) is not complete, hence not a fundamental set. Then there exists an f in $\mathfrak{H}$ such that

$$\sum_{\alpha=1}^{\infty} |(f, \varphi_\alpha)|^2 < \|f\|^2$$

(for otherwise (φ) would be complete). We associate with f the element $g = \sum_{\alpha=1}^{\infty} (f, \varphi_\alpha)\varphi_\alpha$ and note that $f \neq g$. This follows from the fact that $\|g - f_m\| < \delta$ for sufficiently large m, while $\|f - f_m\|$ must be bounded away from zero; for otherwise we could find a subsequence f_{m_ν} such that

$$\|f - f_{m_\nu}\| = \|f\|^2 - \sum_{\alpha=1}^{m_\nu} |(f, \varphi_\alpha)|^2 \to 0 \qquad \text{as} \quad \nu \to \infty$$

and this would imply the completeness equality for f.

Since $f - g \neq 0$, we can form the normalized element $\psi = (f - g)/\|f - g\|$. We claim that ψ is orthogonal to all the φ_α. Indeed, the fact that $f_m \to g$ and the continuity of the scalar product imply that for a fixed but arbitrary α, $(f_m, \varphi_\alpha) \to (g, \varphi_\alpha)$ as $m \to \infty$. For $m > \alpha$, $(f_m, \varphi_\alpha) = \left(\sum_{\beta=1}^{m} (f, \varphi_\beta)\varphi_\beta, \varphi_\alpha\right) = (f, \varphi_\alpha)$. Hence $(f, \varphi_\alpha) = (g, \varphi_\alpha)$, i.e., $(\psi, \varphi_\alpha) = 0$.

We have thus shown that *every orthonormal system can be extended to a larger (complete or incomplete) orthonormal system* by the adjunction of a suitable new element.

If the extended system is still incomplete, we can continue to adjoin new elements in the manner described above. Since an orthonormal system is at most denumerably infinite it follows that *every incomplete orthonormal system can be extended by the adjunction of a finite or denumerably infinite number of elements to a complete orthonormal system.*

It is possible to express the completeness equality in somewhat more general form as follows. Let f and g be arbitrary elements of $\mathfrak{H}$. The completeness equality is equivalent to

$$(f, g) = \sum_{\alpha=1}^{\infty} (f, \varphi_\alpha)(\varphi_\alpha, g).$$

(For $f = g$ we have the original form of the completeness equality.)

To prove this contention we first note that

$$\sum_{\alpha=1}^{\infty} (f+g, \varphi_\alpha)(\varphi_\alpha, f+g) = (f+g, f+g).$$

Expanding the above and employing the completeness relation for f and g we obtain the equality

$$\sum_{\alpha=1}^{\infty} [(f, \varphi_\alpha)(\varphi_\alpha, g) + (g, \varphi_\alpha)(\varphi_\alpha, f)] = (f, g) + (g, f).$$

If we replace f by if, we obtain (after dividing by i) the equality

$$\sum_{\alpha=1}^{\infty} [(f, \varphi_\alpha)(\varphi_\alpha, g) - (g, \varphi_\alpha)(\varphi_\alpha, f)] = (f, g) - (g, f).$$

Addition of these relations yields the desired equality.

4. *Isomorphism between $\mathfrak{H}$ and $\mathfrak{H}_0$*

In conclusion, we deduce the following consequences of the above theorems on complete orthonormal families:

Every Hilbert space $\mathfrak{H}$ is isomorphic to the Hilbert space of sequences, $\mathfrak{H}_0$.

Before clarifying the meaning of this statement we shall show that it is possible to establish a one-to-one correspondence T between the elements in $\mathfrak{H}$ and those in $\mathfrak{H}_0$. To this end we associate with an element f in $\mathfrak{H}$ the sequence of its Fourier coefficients (f, φ_α) with respect to some orthonormal system (φ) in $\mathfrak{H}$. Since $\sum_{\alpha=1}^{\infty} |(f, \varphi_\alpha)|^2$ must converge, $((f, \varphi_1), (f, \varphi_2), \cdots)$ is a definite element in $\mathfrak{H}_0$ and different elements f in $\mathfrak{H}$ define different elements $((f, \varphi_1), (f, \varphi_2), \cdots)$ in $\mathfrak{H}_0$. This shows that the correspondence $T: f \to ((f, \varphi_1), (f, \varphi_2), \cdots)$ is one-to-one into. It remains to show that it is onto.

Let $(x_1, x_2, \cdots)$ be an element in $\mathfrak{H}_0$. Consider the sequence $f_m = \sum_{\alpha=1}^{m} x_\alpha \varphi_\alpha$ of elements in $\mathfrak{H}$. Note that if $m > n$, then $\|f_m - f_n\| = \sum_{\alpha=1}^{m} |x_\alpha|^2$, and this quantity tends to zero as n tends to infinity. This means that the f_m form a Cauchy sequence and, in view of the completeness of $\mathfrak{H}$, there exists a unique element f in $\mathfrak{H}$ such that $f_m \to f$. The continuity of the scalar product implies that $(f, \varphi_\alpha) = \lim_{m\to\infty}(f_m, \varphi_\alpha) = x_\alpha$. We have thus shown that the correspondence

$$T : f \to ((f, \varphi_1), (f, \varphi_2), \cdots)$$

maps the space $\mathfrak{H}$ in a one-to-one manner onto the space $\mathfrak{H}_0$.

We say that a Hilbert space $\mathfrak{H}$ is *isomorphic* to a Hilbert space $\mathfrak{R}$ if there exists a one-to-one mapping T of $\mathfrak{H}$ onto $\mathfrak{R}$ such that

(i) $T(x + y) = Tx + Ty$ for all x, y in $\mathfrak{H}$

(ii) $T(\lambda x) = \lambda T(x)$ for all x in $\mathfrak{H}$ and all scalars λ

(iii) $(Tx, Ty) = (x, y)$ for all x and y in $\mathfrak{H}$.

Having established the existence of a one-to-one correspondence between the spaces $\mathfrak{H}$ and $\mathfrak{H}_0$ we can readily prove their isomorphism. Indeed, conditions (i) and (ii) hold because of the linearity of inner products, while condition (iii) holds because of the completeness relation.

But even the convergence operations in $\mathfrak{H}$ and $\mathfrak{H}_0$ behave "isomorphically": If $f_1, f_2, \cdots$ is a Cauchy sequence in $\mathfrak{H}$ with limit f, then the sequence of images $Tf_1 = \mathfrak{x}_1$, $Tf_2 = \mathfrak{x}_2, \cdots$ under the previously defined isomorphism T is a Cauchy sequence in $\mathfrak{H}_0$ with limit $\mathfrak{x} = Tf$. In fact, putting $T\varphi_\alpha = \mathfrak{e}_\alpha$ we see that $(f_n, \varphi_\alpha) = (\mathfrak{x}_n, \mathfrak{e}_\alpha)$. In view of the continuity of the scalar product operation it follows that

$$(f, \varphi_\alpha) = \lim_{n\to\infty}(f_n, \varphi_\alpha) = \lim_{n\to\infty}(\mathfrak{x}_n, \mathfrak{e}_\alpha) = (\mathfrak{x}, \mathfrak{e}_\alpha).$$

This proves our assertion in the case of strong convergence. In the case of weak convergence, $(f_n, g) \to (f, g)$ for every g in $\mathfrak{H}$. In view of the isomorphism between $\mathfrak{H}$ and $\mathfrak{H}_0$ we have $(\mathfrak{x}_n, \mathfrak{y}) \to (\mathfrak{x}, \mathfrak{y})$ for the corresponding elements in $\mathfrak{H}_0$, and conversely.

In $\mathfrak{H}$, as in $\mathfrak{H}_0$, there are weakly convergent sequences which do not converge strongly. For instance, the sequence of the φ_α converges weakly to 0; indeed, convergence of $\sum_{\alpha=1}^{\infty} |(g, \varphi_\alpha)|^2$ for g in $\mathfrak{H}$ implies that $(\varphi_\alpha, g) \to 0$ as $\alpha \to \infty$. Nevertheless, $\|\varphi_\alpha - 0\| = 1$ for all α.

Because of the isomorphism between $\mathfrak{H}$ and $\mathfrak{H}_0$ we can transfer to $\mathfrak{H}$ all the results we proved for weakly convergent sequences in $\mathfrak{H}_0$. In particular the following result holds:

Every weakly convergent sequence f_n in $\mathfrak{H}$ is bounded, i.e., $\|f_n\| < C$ for all n.

5. More on Weak Convergence

Our previous characterization of a weakly convergent sequence was not intrinsic in the sense that it involved, in addition to the sequence, a limit as well as an arbitrary, fixed element of the space. An intrinsic characterization of weak convergence is given by the following theorem.

A sequence f_n is weakly convergent if and only if $\|f_n\| < C$ and $\lim_{n\to\infty}(f_r, f_n)$ exists for all $r = 1, 2, \cdots$.[6]

We now give a proof of this theorem.[7] Thus, let $f_1, f_2, \cdots$ be weakly convergent to f. Let us orthogonalize this sequence by Schmidt's procedure and let us denote by $\varphi_1, \varphi_2, \cdots$ the resulting system of orthonormal elements. Then every f_n can be represented as a linear combination of the orthonormal elements $\varphi_1, \cdots, \varphi_n$. By adjoining to $\varphi_1, \varphi_2, \cdots$ appropriate elements $\psi_1, \psi_2, \cdots$ we can form a complete orthonormal system. Then every g in $\mathfrak{H}$ can be expressed in the form $\varphi + \psi$, where $\varphi = \sum (g, \varphi_\alpha)\varphi_\alpha$ and $\psi = \sum (g, \psi_\beta)\psi_\beta$. Since we have assumed $f_1, f_2, \cdots$ to be weakly convergent we have

$$(g, f_n) = (\varphi + \psi, f_n) = (\varphi, f_n) \to (\varphi, f) = (g, f)$$

[6] This theorem was first pointed out to me by Prof. E. Schmidt.

[7] In view of the isomorphism between $\mathfrak{H}_0$ and $\mathfrak{H}$, the necessity part of the theorem is obvious. To prove sufficiency, we orthonormalize the f_n to φ_n and then supplement the φ_n to a complete orthonormal basis $\varphi_1, \varphi_2, \cdots, \psi_1, \psi_2, \cdots$ of $\mathfrak{H}$. Again making use of the isomorphism between $\mathfrak{H}_0$ and $\mathfrak{H}$ we can write $f_1 = ((f_1, \varphi_1), (f_1, \varphi_2), \cdots, 0, 0, \cdots)$, $f_2 = ((f_2, \varphi_1), (f_2, \varphi_2), \cdots, 0, 0, \cdots), \cdots$. If $\varphi_1 = \alpha_{11} f_1$, $\varphi_2 = \alpha_{21} f_1 + \alpha_{22} f_2, \cdots$, then we have $f_1 = (\bar{\alpha}_{11}(f_1, f_1), \bar{\alpha}_{21}(f_1, f_1) + \bar{\alpha}_{22}(f_1, f_2), \cdots)$, $f_2 = (\bar{\alpha}_{11}(f_2, f_1), \bar{\alpha}_{21}(f_2, f_1) + \bar{\alpha}_{22}(f_2, f_2), \cdots), \cdots$. Now our assumptions justify the conclusion that $f_1, f_2, \cdots$ converges coordinatewise to an element f in $\mathfrak{H}_0$ (cf. footnote, p. 7). This and the boundedness of the norms of the f_n imply that $f_n \rightharpoonup f$. (Ed.)

(since $(\psi, f_n) = 0$, it follows that $(\psi, f) = 0$). Hence $(\varphi, f_n - f_m) \to 0$ as $n, m \to \infty$. In particular, this implies that $(f_r, f_n - f_m) \to 0$, i.e., $\lim_{n\to\infty}(f_r, f_n)$ exists for $r = 1, 2, \cdots$. Moreover, we know that $\|f_n\| < C$ for all n. This proves necessity. Next we prove sufficiency.

The continuity of scalar products and the orthogonality condition $(\psi, f_n) = 0$ imply the following equality for each element $g = \varphi + \psi$ in $\mathfrak{H}$:

$$(g, f_n - f_m) = \left(\sum_{\alpha=1}^{\infty} (\varphi, \varphi_\alpha)\varphi_\alpha, f_n - f_m\right)$$

$$= \sum_{\alpha=1}^{M} (\varphi, \varphi_\alpha)(\varphi_\alpha, f_n - f_m) + \sum_{\alpha=M+1}^{\infty} (\varphi, \varphi_\alpha)(\varphi_\alpha, f_n - f_m).$$

Since $(\varphi_\alpha, f_n - f_m) \to 0$ as n, m go to infinity, we see that for a fixed M the first summand in the last line above becomes arbitrarily small. By Schwarz's inequality, the second summand is bounded above by

$$\sqrt{\sum_{\alpha=M+1}^{\infty} |(\varphi, \varphi_\alpha)|^2 \cdot \sum_{\alpha=M+1}^{\infty} |(\varphi_\alpha, f_n - f_m)|^2}.$$

By Bessel's inequality, the second factor under the radical sign is $\leqq \|f_n - f_m\|^2 \leqq (\|f_n\| + \|f_m\|)^2 \leqq 4C^2$. As M goes to infinity the above radical goes to zero, implying that as $n, m \to \infty$, $(g, f_n - f_m)$ must go to zero. Hence, as $n \to \infty$, the sequence (g, f_n) converges. For each g in $\mathfrak{H}$ we can therefore define a "functional" $l(g) = \lim_{n\to\infty}(g, f_n)$. This functional is linear, for

$$l(c_1 g_1 + c_2 g_2) = c_1 l(g_1) + c_2 l(g_2)$$

for all scalars c_1 and c_2. Furthermore, $|(g, f_n)| \leqq \|f_n\| \cdot \|g\| \leqq C\|g\|$, whence $|l(g)| \leqq C\|g\|$. We shall now prove that

Every functional $l(g)$ in $\mathfrak{H}$ which is both bounded (i.e., $l(g) \leqq C\|g\|$) and linear (i.e., $l(c_1 g_1 + c_2 g_2) = c_1 l(g_1) + c_2 l(g_2)$) can be thought of as arising from a scalar product, in the sense that there exists an element f in $\mathfrak{H}$ such that

$$l(g) = (g, f).$$

Once this representation theorem has been proved, it can be used to establish our intrinsic characterization of weak convergence, for we then have for every g

$$l(g) = \lim_{n\to\infty}(g, f_n) = (g, f),$$

which shows that the sequence f_n converges weakly to f.

Moreover, the f above must be unique because $(g,f) = (g, f_1)$ for every g implies that f and f_1 must have the same Fourier coefficients with respect to any complete orthonormal family, whence $f = f_1$.

In order to prove the representation theorem stated above, we consider the set $\mathfrak{M}$ of all elements g in $\mathfrak{H}$ for which $l(g) = 0$. If $\mathfrak{M} = \mathfrak{H}$, then $l(g) = (g, 0)$. If $\mathfrak{M} \neq \mathfrak{H}$, then $\mathfrak{M}$ is a subspace of $\mathfrak{H}$, i.e., a subset of $\mathfrak{H}$ which satisfies (as can be easily proved) axioms (a), (b), (c) and sometimes satisfies axiom (d). To prove that (c) holds in $\mathfrak{M}$ we must utilize the continuity of $l(g)$. (The continuity of $l(g)$ is a consequence of its boundedness:

$$|l(g_n) - l(g)| \leqq C\|g_n - g\| \to 0 \qquad \text{as} \quad g_n \to g.)$$

If (d) does not hold, then $\mathfrak{M}$ is finite dimensional. As long as $\mathfrak{M} \neq \mathfrak{H}$, there exists an orthonormal family (ψ) which is complete in $\mathfrak{M}$ but not complete in $\mathfrak{H}$. Let φ be an element orthogonal to all (ψ) and let $f = (l(\varphi)/\|\varphi\|^2)\varphi$. Then the equality $l(g) = (g, f)$ holds not only when g is any element of $\mathfrak{M}$ but also for $g = \varphi$. If g is any element in $\mathfrak{H}$, then $g_1 = g - c\varphi$, with $c = l(g)/l(\varphi)$, lies in $\mathfrak{M}$. Hence

$$\begin{aligned} l(g) = l(g_1 + c\varphi) &= l(g_1) + cl(\varphi) = (g_1, f) + c(\varphi, f) \\ &= (g_1 + c\varphi, f) = (g, f), \quad \text{q.e.d.} \end{aligned}$$

We also have the following theorem:

Given a bounded sequence y_n, with $\|y_n\| \leqq 1$, we can extract a subsequence y_{n_α} such that $y_{n_\alpha} \rightharpoonup y$ and $\|y\| \leqq 1$.

Indeed, we have $|(y_n, y_1)| \leqq \|y_n\| \cdot \|y_1\| \leqq \|y_1\|$ for all n. Hence there exists a subsequence y_{n_α} of y_n such that (y_{n^α}, y_1) converges. From this subsequence we can extract another subsequence y_{m_β} such that (y_{m_β}, y_2) converges. If we continue in this way we obtain a countable number of sequences, each a subsequence of all preceding ones. Let us then consider the diagonal sequence $f_1 = y_{n_1}$, $f_2 = y_{n_2}, \cdots$. For every fixed k the sequence (f_n, y_k) is convergent. In particular, each of the sequences (f_n, f_r) $(r = 1, 2, \cdots)$ converges as $n \to \infty$. Since all $\|f_n\| \leqq 1$, it follows from the theorem just proved that the sequence f_n converges weakly to an element y in $\mathfrak{H}$. It is not difficult to show that $\|y\| \leqq 1$.

Let us examine more closely the concept of a linear subspace of $\mathfrak{H}$. Let $\mathfrak{M}$ be such a subspace and let (ψ) be a complete orthonormal system in $\mathfrak{M}$. As we have previously seen we can extend (ψ) by the adjunction of a system of new elements (φ) to a complete orthonormal system in $\mathfrak{H}$. Let $\mathfrak{N}$ be the subspace of $\mathfrak{H}$ generated by (φ). Then every element f of $\mathfrak{H}$ can be uniquely expressed in the form $f = \psi + \varphi$, where φ belongs to $\mathfrak{N}$ and ψ to $\mathfrak{M}$. In other words, we have decomposed $\mathfrak{H}$ into two subspaces $\mathfrak{M}$ and $\mathfrak{N}$ such that the only element common to $\mathfrak{M}$ and $\mathfrak{N}$ is the zero of $\mathfrak{H}$. We call $\mathfrak{H}$ the direct sum of $\mathfrak{M}$ and $\mathfrak{N}$ and write

$$\mathfrak{H} = \mathfrak{M} \oplus \mathfrak{N}.$$

We call the passage from $\mathfrak{H}$ to $\mathfrak{M}$ (i.e., the map which associates with f the image ψ) the *projection* of $\mathfrak{H}$ on the subspace $\mathfrak{M}$ (along the subspace $\mathfrak{N}$). This is an example of a *linear operator* in $\mathfrak{H}$—a notion which we shall take up in greater detail in Chapter II.

§4. Notes and Exercises to Chapter I

1. Let us consider the set of all continuous functions defined over the interval $a \leqq s \leqq b$. We shall prove that this set is an everywhere dense subspace of $\mathfrak{L}_2(a, b)$. Let us recall that an $\mathfrak{L}_2$-integrable function can, by definition, be approximated in the mean to any desired degree of accuracy by a bounded $\mathfrak{L}_2$-integrable function; that a bounded $\mathfrak{L}_2$-integrable function can be approximated in the mean by a step-function; and that any step function can be so approximated by a continuous function.

It follows that every element in $\mathfrak{L}_2(a, b)$ can be approximated in the mean to any desired degree of accuracy by a continuous function. The continuous functions are not a complete subset of $\mathfrak{L}_2(a, b)$, i.e., there exist Cauchy sequences of continuous functions which do not converge in the mean to continuous functions. By adjoining to each Cauchy sequence of continuous functions an "ideal" limit we obtain a space isomorphic to the space $\mathfrak{L}_2(a, b)$.

2. The system of trigonometric functions (φ_α)

$$\frac{1}{\sqrt{2\pi}}, \quad \frac{1}{\sqrt{\pi}}\cos ns, \quad \frac{1}{\sqrt{\pi}}\sin ns \qquad (n = 1, 2, \cdots)$$

considered over the interval $0 \leqq s \leqq 2\pi$ can easily be shown to be orthonormal. One can also show that if f is continuous and $\int_0^{2\pi} f\varphi_\alpha \, ds = 0$ for all n, then $f = 0$.[8] Furthermore, the completeness relation (with respect to (φ_α)) (cf. p. 18) holds for continuous functions. Indeed, if σ_n denotes the arithmetic mean of the partial sums $s_0, \cdots, s_n$ of the Fourier series of f, then, by Fejer's theorem, we know that for n large enough $|f(t) - \sigma_n(t)| < \delta$, uniformly in t. Using the well-known minimality property of Fourier coefficients we therefore have

$$\int_0^{2\pi} (f(t) - s_n(t))^2 \, dt \leqq \int_0^{2\pi} (f(t) - \sigma_n(t))^2 \, dt < \delta^2 \cdot 2\pi,)$$

and this implies the completeness relation for continuous f. Now by exercise 1 above, the space of continuous f is everywhere dense in $\mathfrak{L}_2(a, b)$, and therefore the completeness relation must hold for all f in $\mathfrak{L}_2(a, b)$. This justifies the conclusion that *the system of trigonometric functions is a complete orthonormal system in* $\mathfrak{L}_2(0, 2\pi)$.

3. We now show that the Hermite functions

$$\varphi_\alpha(s) = \frac{(-1)^\alpha}{\sqrt{2^\alpha \alpha! \sqrt{\pi}}} \exp\left(\frac{s^2}{2}\right) \frac{d^\alpha \exp(-s^2)}{ds^\alpha}$$

[8] See the reference in footnote 5 on p. 13.

constitute a complete orthonormal system over the interval $(-\infty, \infty)$. We first prove a theorem due to Kaczmarz and Steinhaus:[9] Suppose $\omega(t) \geqq 0$, $\omega(t) > 0$ almost everywhere, $v(n) = \int_{-\infty}^{\infty} \omega(t) t^n \, dt$ exists for all $n = 0, 1, 2, \cdots$, and

$$\lim_{n \to \infty} \frac{1}{n} v(2n)^{1/2n} = 0.$$

then $\int_{-\infty}^{\infty} t^{\kappa} f(t) \omega(t) \, dt = 0$ $(\kappa = 0, 1, 2, \cdots)$ and the existence of $\int_{-\infty}^{\infty} |f(t)|^2 \omega(t) \, dt = A^2$ implies that $f(t) = 0$ almost everywhere. To prove this theorem we start from the generalized Schwarz inequality:

$$\left(\int_{-\infty}^{\infty} \omega(t) |t|^{\kappa} |f(t)| \, dt \right)^2 \leqq \int_{-\infty}^{\infty} \omega(t) |f(t)|^2 \, dt \cdot \int_{-\infty}^{\infty} \omega(t) |t|^{2\kappa} \, dt$$

$$= A^2 \; v(2\kappa).$$

Since $\int_{-\infty}^{\infty} \omega(t) |f(t)| \, dt \leqq A \cdot v(0)^{1/2}$, we can define $\Phi(\alpha) = \int_{-\infty}^{\infty} e^{i\alpha t} \omega(t) f(t) \, dt$. Then

$$\Phi(\alpha) = \int_{-\infty}^{\infty} \sum_{\kappa=0}^{\infty} \frac{(i\alpha t)^{\kappa}}{\kappa!} \omega(t) f(t) \, dt$$

$$= \sum_{\kappa=0}^{\infty} \frac{(i\alpha)^{\kappa}}{\kappa!} \int_{-\infty}^{\infty} t^{\kappa} \omega(t) f(t) \, dt.$$

Here we made use of a theorem due to Lebesgue which asserts that if $\left| \sum_{n=1}^{m} \alpha_n(t) \right| \leqq F(t)$ and $F(t)$ belongs to $\mathfrak{L}_1(-\infty, \infty)$, then

$$\int_{-\infty}^{\infty} \sum_{n=0}^{\infty} \alpha_n(t) \, dt = \sum_{n=0}^{\infty} \int_{-\infty}^{\infty} \alpha_n(t) \, dt.$$

Specifically, in our problem

$$\omega(t) |f(t)| \left| \sum_{\kappa=0}^{m} \frac{(i\alpha t)^{\kappa}}{\kappa!} \right| \leqq \sum_{\kappa=0}^{\infty} \frac{|\alpha|^{\kappa} |t|^{\kappa}}{\kappa!} \omega(t) |f(t)| = F(t),$$

[9] "Theorie der Orthogonalreihen." Warszawa-Lwów, 1935.

while the existence of the integral

$$\int_{-\infty}^{\infty} F(t)\,dt = \int_{-\infty}^{\infty} \sum_{\kappa=0}^{\infty} \frac{|\alpha|^{\kappa}|t|^{\kappa}}{\kappa!}\,\omega(t)|f(t)|\,dt$$

$$= \sum_{\kappa=0}^{\infty} \frac{|\alpha|^{\kappa}}{\kappa!} \int_{-\infty}^{\infty} |t|^{\kappa}\omega(t)|f(t)|\,dt$$

follows[10] from the fact that the right side above exists; for it is

$$\leqq \sum_{\kappa=0}^{\infty} \frac{|\alpha|^{\kappa}}{\kappa!}\, v(2\kappa)^{1/2}\cdot A$$

while

$$\lim_{\kappa\to\infty} \sqrt[\kappa]{\frac{v(2\kappa)^{1/2}}{\kappa!}} = \lim_{\kappa\to\infty} \left(\frac{1}{\kappa!}\right)^{1/\kappa} v(2\kappa)^{1/2\kappa}$$

$$= \lim_{\kappa\to\infty} \left(\frac{1}{\sqrt{2\pi}}\,\frac{e^{\kappa}}{\kappa^{\kappa+1/2}}\right)^{1/\kappa} \cdot v(2\kappa)^{1/2\kappa}$$

$$= \lim_{\kappa\to\infty} \frac{e}{\kappa}\cdot v(2\kappa)^{1/2\kappa} = 0.$$

Hence $\Phi(\alpha) = 0$. Using the inverse Fourier transform we find that $f(t) = 0$ almost everywhere, which proves our theorem. (See the exercises at the end of Chapter II for notes on the Fourier transform and its inverse.)

Thus the system of functions t^{κ} is "closed" in the space of all functions $f(t)$ for which $\int_{-\infty}^{\infty} |f(t)|^2\omega(t)\,dt$ exists.[11] This space satisfies the axioms (a), (b), (c), (d) for a Hilbert

[10] The above transformation is justified by a theorem of B. Levi: If $\alpha_{\varkappa} \geqq 0$, then $\int_{-\infty}^{\infty} \sum_{\varkappa=0}^{\infty} \alpha_{\varkappa}(t)\,dt = \sum_{\varkappa=0}^{\infty} \int_{-\infty}^{\infty} \alpha_{\varkappa}(t)\,dt$, in the sense that if one of the expressions on either side of the equality sign exists, so does the other and they are equal; otherwise they both equal ∞. Cf. Sopra l'integrazione delle serie, *Rend. Inst. Lombardo* (2) **39** (1906), 775–786.

[11] I.e., if $\int_{-\infty}^{\infty} t^{\varkappa} f(t)\omega(t)\,dt = 0$ $(\kappa = 0, 1, 2, \cdots)$, then $f(t) = 0$ almost everywhere. This use of the term "closed" should not be confused with the notion of a closed set, meaning a set containing all its limit points. (Ed.)

space provided we define the scalar product by $(f, g) = \int_{-\infty}^{\infty} f(t)\overline{g(t)}\omega(t)\,dt$. We leave it to the reader to show that the closedness of the t^κ implies their completeness, i.e., given any f in $\mathfrak{H}$ we can find a sequence $P_n(t)$ of orthogonal polynomials in $\mathfrak{H}$ such that $\int_{-\infty}^{\infty} |f(t) - P_n(t)|^2\omega(t)\,dt \to 0$ as $n \to \infty$.

If we put $\omega(t) = \exp(-t^2/2)$, then

$$v(2n) = \int_{-\infty}^{\infty} \exp\left(\frac{-t^2}{2}\right) t^{2n}\,dt = \sqrt{2\pi}\,1\cdot 3 \cdots (2n-1),$$

and the conditions of the theorem of Kaczmarz and Steinhaus are satisfied, for

$$\begin{aligned}\lim_{n\to\infty} \frac{1}{n} v(2n)^{1/2n} &= \lim_{n\to\infty} \frac{1}{n}(\sqrt{2\pi}\,1\cdot 3 \cdots (2n-1))^{1/2n} \\ &\leq \lim_{n\to\infty} \frac{1}{n} \sqrt{2\pi}^{1/2n}\cdot(2n)^{n/2n} \\ &\leq \lim_{n\to\infty} \frac{\sqrt{2\pi}}{n}(2n)^{n/2n} = 0.\end{aligned}$$

This proves our original contention concerning the completeness of the Hermite functions on $(-\infty, \infty)$.

4. Completeness of the system of Laguerre functions. These functions are defined by means of the expansion

$$\frac{1}{1-t}\exp\left(-\frac{tx}{1-t}\right) = \sum_{n=0}^{\infty} \frac{t^n}{n!}\mathfrak{L}_n(x), \quad \varphi_n(x) = \frac{\mathfrak{L}_n(x)}{n!}\exp\left(-\frac{x}{2}\right) \qquad (|t| < 1)$$

$$g(x, t) = \frac{1}{1-t}\exp\left(-\frac{1}{2}\frac{1+t}{1-t}x\right) = \sum_{n=0}^{\infty} t^n\varphi_n(x).$$

We see that

$$\int_0^\infty \left(g(x, t) - \sum_{n=0}^{N} t^n\varphi_n(x)\right)^2 dx = \frac{1}{1-t^2} - \sum_{n=0}^{N} t^{2n} \to 0,$$

i.e., for every t with $|t| < 1$, the function $g(x, t)$ can be approximated in $\mathfrak{L}_2(0, \infty)$ to any desired degree of accuracy by the $\varphi_n(x)$. Let us now assume that $f(x)$ is an arbitrary continuous function in $\mathfrak{L}_2(0, \infty)$ equal to zero outside a finite interval. If $\xi = e^{-x}$ then $f(x) = h(\xi)$ is continuous in the interval $0 < \xi \leqq 1$, while for small ξ we have $h(\xi) = 0$. Hence $h(\xi)/\sqrt{\xi}$ is continuous for $0 \leqq \xi \leqq 1$. By Weierstrass' theorem we can approximate $h(\xi)/\sqrt{\xi}$ uniformly over this interval by polynomials, so that

$$\int_0^1 \left(\frac{h(\xi)}{\sqrt{\xi}} - \sum_{\beta=0}^{N} c_\beta \xi^\beta\right)^2 d\xi = \int_0^1 \left(h(\xi) - \sqrt{\xi} \sum_{\beta=0}^{N} c_\beta \xi^\beta\right)^2 \frac{d\xi}{\xi}$$

$$= \int_0^\infty \left(f(x) - e^{-x/2} \sum_{\beta=0}^{N} c_\beta e^{-\beta x}\right)^2 dx < \delta$$

for sufficiently large N.

Hence we have shown that $f(x)$ above (equal to zero outside a closed interval) can be approximated arbitrarily closely in the mean by Laguerre functions. Since the set of these $f(x)$ is dense in $\mathfrak{L}_2(0, \infty)$, it follows that we can approximate all $f(x)$ in $\mathfrak{L}_2(0, \infty)$ arbitrarily closely in the mean by Laguerre functions.

5. Consider the space of continuous functions f defined over the finite interval $a \leqq x \leqq b$. We can define the norm of such an f as $\max|f(x)|$ for x in that interval. The resulting normed space is an instance of a so-called Banach space which is not a Hilbert space, i.e., the norm just mentioned cannot be thought of as arising from a scalar product. Nevertheless, we can define the concept of strong convergence in a Banach space, for this concept depends only on the notion of a norm. We leave it to the reader to prove that convergence in the sense of this norm is identical with the usual uniform convergence of functions. The space in this example is complete.

6. Prove Hoelder's inequality

$$\left|\int_0^1 x(s)y(s)\, ds\right| \leqq \left(\int_0^1 |x(s)|^p\, ds\right)^{1/p}$$

$$\cdot \left(\int_0^1 |y(s)|^q\, ds\right)^{1/q} \qquad \left(\frac{1}{p} + \frac{1}{q} = 1\right)_{p>1,\, q>1},$$

where $x(s)$ is a function in $\mathfrak{L}_p$ while $y(s)$ belongs to $\mathfrak{L}_q$.

Hint: If $A > 0$, $B > 0$, the inequality[12] $x^p/p + y^q/q \geqq xy$ implies

$$\left|\int_0^1 Ax(s)\cdot By(s)\,ds\right| \leqq \frac{A^p}{p}\int_0^1 |x|^p\,ds + \frac{B^q}{q}\int_0^1 |y|^q\,ds = 1,$$

where we put

$$A = \frac{1}{\sqrt[p]{\int_0^1 |x|^p\,ds}}, \qquad B = \frac{1}{\sqrt[q]{\int_0^1 |y|^q\,ds}}.$$

Also prove Minkowski's inequality:[13]

$$\sqrt[p]{\int_0^1 |x+y|^p\,ds} \leqq \sqrt[p]{\int_0^1 |x|^p\,ds} + \sqrt[p]{\int_0^1 |y|^p\,ds}.$$

7. Prove that the elements y in the Hilbert space $\mathfrak{L}_2$ whose pth powers are $\mathfrak{L}$ integrable (where p is an integer > 1) constitute a Banach space $\mathfrak{L}_p$ satisfying axioms (a) and (c) provided we use the norm $\|y\| = \sqrt[p]{\int_0^1 |y|^p\,ds}$. Note that this norm satisfies the triangle inequality. Show that the integrals $\int_0^1 y^\alpha\,ds$, $0 < \alpha < p$, exist. Hence if $y_n \to y$ in $\mathfrak{L}_2$, then $y_n^\alpha \to y^\alpha$ $(0 < 2\alpha < p)$ in $\mathfrak{L}_2$. However, if the sequence y_n converges weakly to y in $\mathfrak{L}_p$ (this means that $\lim_{n\to\infty} \int_0^1 (y_n - y)z\,ds = 0$ for all z in $\mathfrak{L}_q$ where $(1/p) + (1/q) = 1$), it does not always follow that $y_n^\alpha \rightharpoonup y^\alpha$. Counterexample: In the interval $0 \leqq x \leqq 2\pi$, $\sin nx \rightharpoonup 0$ but $\sin^2 nx \rightharpoonup \frac{1}{2}$.

[12] Consider the curves $x = y^{q-1}$ and $y = x^{p-1}$ and compare appropriate areas.

[13] Decompose the integrand on the left by factoring out $|x+y|$, use the triangle inequality, and then use the Hoelder inequality.

II. LINEAR OPERATORS IN $\mathfrak{H}$

§5. Bounded Linear Operators in $\mathfrak{H}$ and Their Principal Properties. Biorthogonal Systems

1. Bounded Linear Operators

A map $\mathfrak{K}$ which associates with each element y belonging to a subset $\mathfrak{D}$ of $\mathfrak{H}$ an element $\mathfrak{K}_y$ belonging to a Hilbert space $\mathfrak{H}'$ is said to be an operator with domain of definition $\mathfrak{D}$. $\mathfrak{H}$ need not be distinct from $\mathfrak{H}'$.

If the following two conditions are satisfied we call $\mathfrak{K}$ a linear operator:

(a) $\mathfrak{D}$ is a linear manifold, i.e., if y_1 and y_2 belong to $\mathfrak{D}$ so does $(c_1 y_1 + c_2 y_2)$, for any complex numbers c_1 and c_2.

(b) $\mathfrak{K}(c_1 y_1 + c_2 y_2) = c_1 \mathfrak{K} y_1 + c_2 \mathfrak{K} y_2$.

A linear operator $\mathfrak{K}$ with domain of definition $\mathfrak{H}$ is said to be bounded if there exists a constant $C \geqq 0$ such that $\|\mathfrak{K}y\| \leqq C\|y\|$ for all y in $\mathfrak{H}$. There always exists a smallest C of this kind—it is called the norm of $\mathfrak{K}$ and is denoted by $\|\mathfrak{K}\|$.

Whenever $\mathfrak{K}$ is a bounded operator we can define its adjoint operator $\mathfrak{K}^*$ on $\mathfrak{H}'$ by means of the following equality:

$$(\mathfrak{K}y, x) = (y, \mathfrak{K}^* x) \qquad \text{for any } y \text{ in } \mathfrak{H} \text{ and } x \text{ in } \mathfrak{H}'.$$

In fact, for a fixed x the scalar product $(\mathfrak{K}y, x)$ is a bounded linear functional in y and hence, by §3, representable in the form (y, f). This means that with each x we can associate an f, and this association is a linear operator defined in $\mathfrak{H}'$. We designate this operator by the symbol $\mathfrak{K}^*$, so that $(\mathfrak{K}y, x) = (y, f) = (y, \mathfrak{K}^* x)$.

From $\|\mathfrak{K}y\| \leqq \|\mathfrak{K}\| \cdot \|y\|$ it follows that $(\mathfrak{K}y, x)$ is bounded, i.e., $|(\mathfrak{K}y, x)| \leqq \|\mathfrak{K}y\| \cdot \|x\| \leqq \|\mathfrak{K}\| \cdot \|y\| \cdot \|x\|$ for every pair of elements

x, y in $\mathfrak{H}'$ and $\mathfrak{H}$, respectively. Conversely, if $|(\mathfrak{K}y, x)| \leqq C\|x\| \cdot \|y\|$, and if we put $x = \mathfrak{K}y$, then

$$\|\mathfrak{K}y\|^2 \leqq C\|\mathfrak{K}y\| \cdot \|y\|,$$

i.e., either $\mathfrak{K}y = 0$ or $\|\mathfrak{K}y\| \leqq C\|y\|$; in any case this last inequality always holds and signifies that $\mathfrak{K}$ is bounded. Hence, if we define the norm of $(\mathfrak{K}y, x)$ as the least number C such that $|(\mathfrak{K}y, x)| \leqq C \cdot \|y\| \cdot \|x\|$, then the boundedness of $\mathfrak{K}$ is equivalent to the boundedness of the function $(\mathfrak{K}y, x)$ with norm equal to the norm of $\mathfrak{K}$.

If $\mathfrak{K}$ is a bounded operator, so is its adjoint $\mathfrak{K}^*$. Since

$$(\mathfrak{K}y, x) = (y, \mathfrak{K}^*x),$$

$\mathfrak{K}$ and $\mathfrak{K}^*$ have the same norms, $\|\mathfrak{K}\| = \|\mathfrak{K}^*\|$.

We shall show that *if the domain of definition* $\mathfrak{D}$ *of the linear operator* $\mathfrak{K}$ *is all of* $\mathfrak{H}$ *and if* $\mathfrak{K}^*$ *exists and has all of* $\mathfrak{H}'$ *as its domain of definition, then* $\mathfrak{K}$ *and* $\mathfrak{K}^*$ *are both bounded.*

In fact, if $x_n \rightharpoonup 0$ in $\mathfrak{H}'$, then for every fixed y, $(\mathfrak{K}y, x_n) \to 0$. Hence $(y, \mathfrak{K}^*x_n) \to 0$, i.e., $\mathfrak{K}^*x_n$ converges weakly to zero. Conversely, if $y_n \rightharpoonup 0$ in $\mathfrak{H}$, then $\mathfrak{K}y_n \rightharpoonup 0$. Now let $y_n \to y$ in $\mathfrak{H}$. For every fixed x we see that $|(\mathfrak{K}(y_n - y), x)| = |(y_n - y, \mathfrak{K}^*x)| \leqq \|y_n - y\| \cdot \|\mathfrak{K}^*x\|$. In particular, for $x = \mathfrak{K}(y_n - y)$ we get the inequality

$$\|\mathfrak{K}(y_n - y)\|^2 \leqq \|y_n - y\| \cdot \|\mathfrak{K}^*(\mathfrak{K}(y_n - y))\|.$$

Since $y_n - y \rightharpoonup 0$, it follows that $\mathfrak{K}(y_n - y) \rightharpoonup 0$. This, in turn, implies that $\mathfrak{K}^*(\mathfrak{K}(y_n - y)) \rightharpoonup 0$. Hence this sequence is bounded. This fact and the last inequality above show that as $n \to \infty$, $\|\mathfrak{K}(y_n - y)\| \to 0$, i.e., $\mathfrak{K}y_n \to \mathfrak{K}y$. This means that $\mathfrak{K}$ is a continuous operator (with respect to strong convergence).

We now complete the proof of our theorem by establishing the following result: *Every continuous linear operator defined on all of* $\mathfrak{H}$ *must be bounded.* Indeed, if this were not the case, then there would exist a sequence y_n such that $\|\mathfrak{K}y_n\| \geqq n\|y_n\|$. If we put $z_n = y_n/n\|y_n\|$, then on the one hand we would have $z_n \to 0$, and on the other hand $\|\mathfrak{K}z_n\| \geqq 1$, contradicting the continuity of $\mathfrak{K}$. Hence $\mathfrak{K}$ (and likewise $\mathfrak{K}^*$) must be bounded.

If $\mathfrak{K}$ and $\mathfrak{L}$ are two bounded operators which map $\mathfrak{H}$ into $\mathfrak{H}$, then we can define the product operator $\mathfrak{K}\mathfrak{L}$ by means of the equation: $(\mathfrak{K}\mathfrak{L})y = \mathfrak{K}(\mathfrak{L}y)$. $\mathfrak{K}\mathfrak{L}$ is also bounded and, furthermore, $\|\mathfrak{K}\mathfrak{L}\| \leqq \|\mathfrak{K}\| \cdot \|\mathfrak{L}\|$. We also see immediately that $(\mathfrak{K}\mathfrak{L})^* = \mathfrak{L}^*\mathfrak{K}^*$. In general $\mathfrak{K}\mathfrak{L} \neq \mathfrak{L}\mathfrak{K}$. If $\mathfrak{K}\mathfrak{L} = \mathfrak{L}\mathfrak{K}$, then we say that the operators $\mathfrak{K}$ and $\mathfrak{L}$ commute and write $\mathfrak{K} \mathrm{c} \mathfrak{L}$.

If $\mathfrak{K}$ is a bounded operator, then we can reduce the problem of solving the operator equation $\mathfrak{K}y = x$ to the problem of solving a system of infinitely many linear equations with complex coefficients in an infinite number of unknowns. To do this we choose two complete orthonormal families $\varphi_1, \varphi_2, \cdots$ in $\mathfrak{H}'$ and $\psi_1, \psi_2, \cdots$ in $\mathfrak{H}$. If we put

$$(x, \varphi_\alpha) = x_\alpha, \qquad (y, \psi_\beta) = y_\beta,$$

then, by the completeness equality, $\mathfrak{K}y = x$ implies

$$x_\alpha = (\mathfrak{K}y, \varphi_\alpha) = (y, \mathfrak{K}^*\varphi_\alpha) = \sum_{\beta=1}^{\infty} (y, \psi_\beta)(\psi_\beta, \mathfrak{K}^*\varphi_\alpha)$$
$$= \sum_{\beta=1}^{\infty} (\mathfrak{K}\psi_\beta, \varphi_\alpha) y_\beta \qquad (\alpha = 1, 2, \cdots).$$

The matrix $A = (a_{\alpha\beta}) = (\mathfrak{K}\psi_\beta, \varphi_\alpha)$ is known as the kernel matrix[1] of the operator $\mathfrak{K}$ with respect to the two orthonormal families (φ) and (ψ). If y is a solution of our operator equation $\mathfrak{K}y = x$, then the y_β satisfy the associated linear system. As for the converse, let us first note that the x_α appearing on the left side of our linear system can be thought of as the components of a vector. Suppose that our system admits a solution in the y_β such that the sum of the absolute values of the squares of the y_β is convergent. Then if we put $y = \sum_{\beta=1}^{\infty} y_\beta \psi_\beta$ we have

$$x_\alpha = \sum_{\beta=1}^{\infty} (\mathfrak{K}\psi_\beta, \varphi_\alpha)(y, \psi_\beta) = \sum_{\beta=1}^{\infty} (\psi_\beta, \mathfrak{K}^*\varphi_\alpha)(y, \psi_\beta) = (y, \mathfrak{K}^*\varphi_\alpha)$$
$$= (\mathfrak{K}y, \varphi_\alpha).$$

Hence $x = \sum_{\alpha=1}^{\infty} x_\alpha \varphi_\alpha = \mathfrak{K}y$. Our *operator equation and its associated system of linear equations are therefore equivalent.*

[1] This terminology comes from the integral operator $\int_a^b \mathfrak{K}(s, t)y(t)\,dt$ in which case $\mathfrak{K}(s, t)$ is usually called the kernel.

This is nothing more than a consequence of the fact that $\mathfrak{H}$ is isomorphic to $\mathfrak{H}_0$ and $\mathfrak{H}'$ is isomorphic to $\mathfrak{H}_0'$. The supposition that $\mathfrak{K}$ is bounded is equivalent to the boundedness of its associated kernel matrix, by which we mean the boundedness of the form defined by that matrix. In fact, for each y in $\mathfrak{H}$ and each x in $\mathfrak{H}'$ we have

$$(\mathfrak{K}y, x) = \sum_{\alpha=1}^{\infty} (\mathfrak{K}y, \varphi_\alpha)(\varphi_\alpha, x) = \sum_{\alpha=1}^{\infty} \bar{x}_\alpha(y, \mathfrak{K}^*\varphi_\alpha)$$

and on the other hand

$$(y, \mathfrak{K}^*\varphi_\alpha) = \sum_{\beta=1}^{\infty} (y, \psi_\beta)(\psi_\beta, \mathfrak{K}^*\varphi_\alpha) = \sum_{\beta=1}^{\infty} a_{\alpha\beta} y_\beta.$$

Hence

$$(\mathfrak{K}y, x) = \sum_{\alpha=1}^{\infty} \bar{x}_\alpha \left(\sum_{\beta=1}^{\infty} a_{\alpha\beta} y_\beta \right)$$

and, in view of the boundedness of $\mathfrak{K}$,

$$\left| \sum_{\alpha=1}^{\infty} \bar{x}_\alpha \left(\sum_{\beta=1}^{\infty} a_{\alpha\beta} y_\beta \right) \right| \leqq \|\mathfrak{K}\| \sqrt{\sum_{\alpha=1}^{\infty} |x_\alpha|^2 \cdot \sum_{\beta=1}^{\infty} |y_\beta|^2}.$$

Conversely, a bounded matrix $(a_{\alpha\beta})$ represents a bounded operator on the Hilbert space $\mathfrak{H}_0$ of sequences $(y_1, y_2, \cdots)$.[2]

Since $(\mathfrak{K}y, x) = (y, \mathfrak{K}^*x)$ we also have

$$\sum_{\alpha=1}^{\infty} \bar{x}_\alpha \left(\sum_{\beta=1}^{\infty} a_{\alpha\beta} y_\beta \right) = \sum_{\beta=1}^{\infty} y_\beta \left(\sum_{\alpha=1}^{\infty} a_{\alpha\beta} \bar{x}_\alpha \right) = \sum_{\beta=1}^{\infty} y_\beta \cdot \overline{\left(\sum_{\alpha=1}^{\infty} \bar{a}_{\alpha\beta} x_\alpha \right)}$$

and the kernel matrix associated with $\mathfrak{K}^*$ is $A^* = (\bar{a}_{\beta\alpha})$. The transition from an operator equation to an equivalent system of

[2] *Proof. Lemma* (Landau). If $\sum_{\alpha=1}^{\infty} u_\alpha c_\alpha$ converges for all $(u_1, u_2, \cdots)$ in H_0, then $(c_1, c_2, \cdots)$ is in $\mathfrak{H}_0$.

Now consider the form $\sum_{\alpha=1}^{\infty} \bar{x}_\alpha (\sum_{\beta=1}^{\infty} a_{\alpha\beta} y_\beta) = \sum_{\alpha=1}^{\infty} \bar{x}_\alpha c_\alpha$. By the lemma just stated $(c_1, c_2, \cdots)$ is in $\mathfrak{H}_0$. Hence the operator which takes $(y_1, y_2, \cdots)$ in $\mathfrak{H}_0$ into $(c_1, c_2, \cdots)$ is a linear operator which maps $\mathfrak{H}_0$ into $\mathfrak{H}_0$. Its boundedness is a direct consequence of the assumed boundedness of the matrix $(a_{\alpha\beta})$, i.e., of the bilinear form defined by this matrix (cf. pp. 32, 33). (Ed.)

linear equations is especially important in the study of the integral equation

$$\mathfrak{K}y = \int_a^b K(s, t)y(t)\, dt = x(s) \qquad (c \leqq s \leqq d),$$

in which the given function $x(s)$ belongs to the Hilbert space $\mathfrak{L}_2(c, d)$ while the unknown function $y(t)$ belongs to the Hilbert space $\mathfrak{L}_2(a, b)$.[3]

If the linear operator $\mathfrak{K}$ is defined for all y belonging to a dense subset $\mathfrak{D}$ of $\mathfrak{H}$ and $\|\mathfrak{K}y\| \leqq \|\mathfrak{K}\| \cdot \|y\|$, i.e., if $\mathfrak{K}$ is bounded on $\mathfrak{D}$, then we can extend the definition of $\mathfrak{K}$ uniquely to the whole space in such a way that the extended $\mathfrak{K}$ is also bounded.

For if y is an element of $\mathfrak{H}$ then there exists a sequence of elements $y_1, y_2, \cdots$ all lying in $\mathfrak{D}$ such that this sequence converges strongly to y. Then $\|\mathfrak{K}(y_n - y_m\| \leqq \|\mathfrak{K}\| \cdot \|y_n - y_m\| \to 0$ as $n, m \to \infty$. Hence the sequence $\|\mathfrak{K}y_n\|$ is convergent and $\mathfrak{K}y_n$ therefore converges strongly to an element z in $\mathfrak{H}'$, where z depends only on y.[4] If we put $\mathfrak{K}y = z$, then the domain of definition of our operator is extended to all of $\mathfrak{H}$. Since

$$\|\mathfrak{K}y_n\| \leqq \|\mathfrak{K}\| \cdot \|y_n\|,$$

it follows that

$$\|\mathfrak{K}y\| \leqq \|\mathfrak{K}\| \cdot \|y\|.$$

Since y was an arbitrary element of $\mathfrak{H}$, we conclude that $\mathfrak{K}$ is bounded on all of $\mathfrak{H}$ with the same norm $\|\mathfrak{K}\|$ as in $\mathfrak{D}$. This extension is clearly unique.

2. *Biorthogonal Systems*

We conclude this section with a discussion of biorthogonal systems, a generalization of orthogonal systems. By a bior-

[3] At this point the author refers the reader to his work on integral equations. A recent and extensive English work on the subject of integral equations is F. Smithies, "Integral Equations." Cambridge Univ. Press. (Ed.)

[4] To see that z depends only on y, consider $y_n \to y$, $y_n' \to y$, and then a third sequence, $w_n \to y$, obtained by interspersing y_n and y_n'. (Ed.)

thogonal system we mean a finite or countably infinite system of elements in $\mathfrak{H}$, $u_1, u_2, \cdots ; v_1, v_2, \cdots$ such that

$$(u_\alpha, v_\beta) = \delta_{\alpha\beta} = \begin{cases} 0 & (\alpha \neq \beta) \\ 1 & (\alpha = \beta) \end{cases}.$$

Biorthogonal systems exist, for two replicas of an orthogonal system form a biorthogonal system.

Note that *the elements u_α are linearly independent, as are the v_α*; for if

$$c_1 u_1 + \cdots + c_n u_n = 0,$$

with constant coefficients c_α, then

$$\sum_{\alpha=1}^{n} c_\alpha (u_\alpha, v_\beta) = c_\beta = 0 \qquad (\beta = 1, \cdots, n).$$

The linear independence of the v_α is proved in a similar manner.

Given any finite system of linearly independent elements $u_1, u_2, \cdots, u_n$ we can always find a system $v_1, v_2, \cdots, v_n$ such that these two systems are biorthogonal. To prove this contention let us first orthogonalize the u_α so that we have, say,

$$u_\alpha = \sum_{\beta=1}^{\alpha} a_{\alpha\beta} \varphi_\beta, \qquad a_{\alpha\alpha} \neq 0.$$

Solving this system for the φ_α we get a system of the form

$$\varphi_\alpha = \sum_{\gamma=1}^{\alpha} A_{\alpha\gamma} u_\gamma.$$

If we define

$$v_\beta = \sum_{\alpha=1}^{n} \bar{A}_{\alpha\beta} \varphi_\alpha,$$

we see that

$$(u_\alpha, v_\beta) = \left(\sum_{\gamma=1}^{\alpha} a_{\alpha\gamma} \varphi_\gamma, \sum_{\lambda=1}^{n} \bar{A}_{\lambda\beta} \varphi_\lambda \right) = \sum_{\gamma=1}^{n} a_{\alpha\gamma} A_{\gamma\beta} = \delta_{\alpha\beta}$$

$$(\alpha, \beta = 1, 2, \cdots, n).$$

The question now arises as to whether every *infinite* system of linearly independent vectors $u_1, u_2, \cdots$ can be extended to a biorthogonal system. This is not always possible. For if $u_1, u_2, \cdots$ are linearly independent and if, as in Schmidt's orthogonalization procedure,

$$u_\alpha = \sum_{\beta=1}^{\alpha} a_{\alpha\beta}\varphi_\beta \qquad (\alpha = 1, 2, \cdots),$$

then once again we have

$$\varphi_\alpha = \sum_{\gamma=1}^{\alpha} A_{\alpha\gamma}u_\gamma.$$

Here $(a_{\alpha\beta})$ and $(A_{\alpha\beta})$ are both "triangular" matrices and each is a left and right inverse of the other. However, in general, the definition of v_β leads to difficulties, since

$$v_\beta = \sum_{\alpha=1}^{\infty} \bar{A}_{\alpha\beta}\varphi_\alpha$$

can represent an element in $\mathfrak{H}$ if and only if $\sum_{\alpha=1}^{\infty} |A_{\alpha\beta}|^2$ converges. If this is the case, then we have, as above,

$$(u_\alpha, v_\beta) = \sum_{\gamma=1}^{\infty} (u_\alpha, \varphi_\gamma)(\varphi_\gamma, v_\beta) = \sum_{\gamma=1}^{\alpha} a_{\alpha\gamma}A_{\gamma\beta} = \delta_{\alpha\beta} \qquad (\alpha, \beta = 1, 2, \cdots).$$

Thus, *a linearly independent system of elements $u_1, u_2, \cdots$ in $\mathfrak{H}$ can be extended to a biorthogonal system if and only if the coefficients $A_{\alpha\gamma}$ which arise in the orthogonalization of the u_γ when we form $\varphi_\alpha = \sum_{\gamma=1}^{\alpha} A_{\alpha\gamma}u_\gamma$ are such that $\sum_{\alpha=1}^{\infty} |A_{\alpha\gamma}|^2$ converges for $\gamma = 1, 2, \cdots$.*

This last condition is surely satisfied if the matrix $(A_{\alpha\beta})$ is bounded.[5] If both $(A_{\alpha\beta})$ and $(a_{\alpha\beta})$ are bounded matrices we speak of a bounded biorthogonal system. Bounded biorthogonal systems exist, since two replicas of an orthonormal system form a bounded biorthogonal system with $a_{\alpha\beta} = A_{\alpha\beta} = \delta_{\alpha\beta}$.

[5] *Proof.* Let $(A_{\alpha\beta})$ be a bounded matrix. This means that the form $\sum_{\alpha=1}^{\infty} \bar{x}_\alpha(\sum_{\beta=1}^{\infty} A_{\alpha\beta}y_\beta)$ is bounded (for all $(x_1, x_2, \cdots)$ and $(y_1, y_2, \cdots)$ in $\mathfrak{H}_0$). It follows (cf. p. 35) that the operator $\mathfrak{A}$ which takes $\mathfrak{y} = (y_1, y_2, \cdots)$ into $\mathfrak{A}\mathfrak{y} = (c_1, c_2, \cdots)$ with $c_\alpha = \sum_{\beta=1}^{\infty} A_{\alpha\beta}y_\beta$ is a linear operator which maps $\mathfrak{H}_0$ into $\mathfrak{H}_0$. If $\mathfrak{y} = \mathfrak{e}_\gamma$ (the γth unit vector), then $\|\mathfrak{A}\mathfrak{e}_\gamma\|^2 = \sum_{\alpha=1}^{\infty} |A_{\alpha\gamma}|^2$. (Ed.)

A biorthogonal system is said to be complete if the $u_1, u_2, \cdots$ and the $v_1, v_2, \cdots$ are fundamental sets in $\mathfrak{H}$. In this connection we have the following theorem:

Any element f in $\mathfrak{H}$ can be represented by means of a bounded complete biorthogonal system as follows:

$$f = \sum_{\alpha=1}^{\infty} (f, v_\alpha)u_\alpha = \sum_{\beta=1}^{\infty} (f, u_\beta)v_\beta.$$

Here the series $\sum_{\alpha=1}^{\infty} |(f, v_\alpha)|^2$ and $\sum_{\beta=1}^{\infty} |(f, u_\beta)|^2$ converge. Conversely, if the series $\sum_{\alpha=1}^{\infty} |x_\alpha|^2$ and $\sum_{\beta=1}^{\infty} |y_\beta|^2$ converge, then $\sum_{\alpha=1}^{\infty} x_\alpha u_\alpha$ and $\sum_{\beta=1}^{\infty} y_\beta v_\beta$ represent elements in $\mathfrak{H}$.

For proof, let us consider the operator which associates with each element $\sum x_\alpha \varphi_\alpha$ with Fourier coefficients x_α with respect to the complete orthonormal system (φ), the element $\sum x_\alpha u_\alpha$ with the Fourier coefficients $\sum_{\alpha=1}^{\infty} x_\alpha a_{\alpha\beta}$. Let us call this operator $\mathfrak{A}$. $\mathfrak{A}$ is linear and bounded. We have $u_\alpha = \mathfrak{A}\varphi_\alpha$. If we put $u = \mathfrak{A}x$, then for every u in $\mathfrak{H}$, $x = \mathfrak{A}^{-1}u$. $\mathfrak{A}^{-1}$ is also a bounded operator. From $(u_\alpha, v_\beta) = \delta_{\alpha\beta}$ it follows that $(\mathfrak{A}\varphi_\alpha, v_\beta) = (\varphi_\alpha, \mathfrak{A}^* v_\beta) = \delta_{\alpha\beta}$ and therefore $\mathfrak{A}^* v_\beta = \varphi_\beta$, i.e., $v_\beta = \mathfrak{A}^{*-1}\varphi_\beta$. Hence $(f, v_\alpha) = (f, \mathfrak{A}^{*-1}\varphi_\alpha) = (\mathfrak{A}^{-1}f, \varphi_\alpha)$ and we have the representation

$$\mathfrak{A}^{-1}f = \sum_{\alpha=1}^{\infty} (f, v_\alpha)\varphi_\alpha$$

$$f = \mathfrak{A}\left(\sum_{\alpha=1}^{\infty} (f, v_\alpha)\varphi_\alpha\right) = \sum_{\alpha=1}^{\infty} (f, v_\alpha)\mathfrak{A}\varphi_\alpha = \sum_{\alpha=1}^{\infty} (f, v_\alpha)u_\alpha.$$

In interchanging the order of $\mathfrak{A}$ and $\sum$ in the last equation we made use of the continuity of $\mathfrak{A}$. The representation $f = \sum_{\alpha=1}^{\infty} (f, u_\alpha)v_\alpha$ is obtained in a similar manner.

As for the remaining assertions note that the absolute value of each sum $\sum_{\alpha=n+1}^{m} x_\alpha u_\alpha = \sum_{\alpha=n+1}^{m} x_\alpha \mathfrak{A}\varphi_\alpha$ is bounded above by $\|\mathfrak{A}\|\sqrt{\sum_{\alpha=n+1}^{m} |x_\alpha|^2}$, which itself goes to zero as $n, m \to \infty$ provided that $\sum_{\alpha=1}^{\infty} |x_\alpha|^2$ converges; consequently, the partial sums $\sum_{\alpha=1}^{m} x_\alpha u_\alpha$ converge strongly to a limit in $\mathfrak{H}$. The same conclusions hold for $\sum_{\beta=1}^{\infty} y_\beta v_\beta$. This completes the proof of our theorem.

For every bounded complete biorthogonal system the following completeness relations hold:

$$(f, g) = \sum_{\alpha=1}^{\infty} (f, u_\alpha)(v_\alpha, g) = \sum_{\beta=1}^{\infty} (f, v_\beta)(u_\beta, g).$$

For, as above, we must have

$$(f, u_\alpha) = (f, \mathfrak{A}\varphi_\alpha) = (\mathfrak{A}^* f, \varphi_\alpha), (v_\alpha, g) = (\varphi_\alpha, \mathfrak{A}^{-1} g),$$

and hence

$$\sum_{\alpha=1}^{\infty} (f, u_\alpha)(v_\alpha, g) = \sum_{\alpha=1}^{\infty} (\mathfrak{A}^* f, \varphi_\alpha)(\varphi_\alpha, \mathfrak{A}^{-1} g)$$

$$= (\mathfrak{A}^* f, \mathfrak{A}^{-1} g) = (f, g).$$

The second completeness relation follows by similar reasoning.

Every bounded linear operator $u = \mathfrak{A}x$ possessing an inverse $x = \mathfrak{A}^{-1}u$ which itself is bounded and linear generates a complete bounded biorthogonal system by means of the defining equations $\mathfrak{A}\varphi_\alpha = u_\alpha$, $\mathfrak{A}^{*-1}\varphi_\beta = v_\beta$, provided that the φ_α form a complete orthonormal family. The converse is also true.

This theorem is an immediate consequence of the previous discussion in which we made use of the boundedness of $\mathfrak{A}$ and $\mathfrak{A}^{-1}$ but not of the "triangular" character of the matrices $(a_{\alpha\beta})$ and $(A_{\alpha\beta})$. Among other things, this theorem implies that for a bounded biorthogonal system to be complete it suffices that one of the two families u_α or v_β be a fundamental set; for if one is fundamental then so is the other.

Let us now consider incomplete bounded biorthogonal systems. Such systems can be characterized by the fact that the φ_α which arise by orthogonalizing the u_α constitute an incomplete orthonormal system. In this case orthogonalization of the v_β cannot lead to a complete orthonormal system. Hence there must exist elements f which are orthogonal to all the v_β. The set generated by all these f satisfies all three conditions (a), (b), (c) and so forms a subspace of $\mathfrak{H}$. Let $f_1, f_2, \cdots$ be a complete orthonormal family in this subspace. Now, if f is any element in the space $\mathfrak{H}$, f can be represented in the form $\sum_{\beta=1}^{\infty} y_\beta v_\beta +$

$\sum_{(\alpha)}(f, f_\alpha)f_\alpha$, where $\sum_{\beta=1}^{\infty}|y_\beta|^2$ converges, and all $\sum_{\beta=1}^{\infty} y_\beta v_\beta$ for which $\sum_{\beta=1}^{\infty}|y_\beta|^2$ converges belong to $\mathfrak{H}$.

We now prove the following theorem:

The system $u_1, u_2, \cdots, f_1, f_2, \cdots$ forms together with $v_1, \ v_2, \cdots,$

$$g_1 = f_1 - \sum_{\beta=1}^{\infty}(f_1, u_\beta)v_\beta, \qquad g_2 = f_2 - \sum_{\beta=1}^{\infty}(f_2, u_\beta)v_\beta, \cdots$$

a complete bounded biorthogonal system. Thus every incomplete bounded biorthogonal system can be extended to a complete bounded biorthogonal system.

To begin with we must show that $g_1, g_2, \cdots$ are well-defined elements of $\mathfrak{H}$. In fact, $u_\beta = \mathfrak{A}\varphi_\beta$, so that $(f, u_\alpha) = (\mathfrak{A}^*f, \varphi_\alpha)$ for f in $\mathfrak{H}$. In view of the boundedness of $\mathfrak{A}^*$ we may therefore conclude that $\sum_{\beta=1}^{\infty}|(f, u_\beta)|^2$ converges, so that $g_1, g_2, \cdots$ are elements of $\mathfrak{H}$. Next

$$(u_\alpha, v_\beta) = \delta_{\alpha\beta}, \qquad (f_\alpha, v_\beta) = 0,$$

$$(u_\alpha, g_\gamma) = (u_\alpha, f_\gamma) - (u_\alpha, f_\gamma) = 0,$$

$$(f_\alpha, g_\gamma) = (f_\alpha, f_\gamma) = \delta_{\alpha\gamma}.$$

Furthermore, if f is an arbitrary element in $\mathfrak{H}$, then $f - \sum_{\beta=1}^{\infty}(f, v_\beta)u_\beta$ is orthogonal to each v_β and must therefore lie in the subspace of the f_α. Hence the u_α and f_α, taken together, form a fundamental set and the same is true for the v_α and g_α. Hence our biorthogonal system is complete. We claim that it is also bounded. In order to establish this, let us now understand by $\mathfrak{A}^{-1}$ the operator associated with the whole system $u_1, u_2, \cdots,$ $f_1, f_2, \cdots$. This operator is defined in all of $\mathfrak{H}$ and the same is true of its adjoint $\mathfrak{A}^{*-1}$. To see that $\mathfrak{A}^{-1}$ is defined in all of $\mathfrak{H}$ note that every f in $\mathfrak{H}$ can be written as $f = \sum_{\beta=1}^{\infty}(f, v_\beta)u_\beta + \sum_{\alpha=1}^{\infty}(f, g_\alpha)f_\alpha$, where $\sum_{\beta=1}^{\infty}|(f, v_\beta)|^2 + \sum_{\alpha=1}^{\infty}|(f, g_\alpha)|^2$ converges; the first summand converges by hypothesis and the second because

$$(f, g_\alpha) = \left(f, f_\alpha - \sum_{\gamma=1}^{\infty}(f_\alpha, u_\gamma)v_\gamma\right) = (f, f_\alpha) - \sum_{\gamma=1}^{\infty}(f, v_\gamma)(u_\gamma, f_\alpha)$$

$$= (f, f_\alpha) - \left(\sum_{\gamma=1}^{\infty}(f, v_\gamma)u_\gamma, f_\alpha\right) = \left(f - \sum_{\gamma=1}^{\infty}(f, v_\gamma)u_\gamma, f_\alpha\right)$$

are Fourier coefficients. Consequently, $\|\mathfrak{A}^{-1}f\|$ is finite for all f. It now follows (cf. the theorem on p. 33) that $\mathfrak{A}^{-1}$ must be bounded. In similar fashion we can prove the same result for $\mathfrak{A}$. Namely, for every f in $\mathfrak{H}$

$$f = \sum_{\beta=1}^{\infty} (f, u_\beta)v_\beta + \sum_{\beta=1}^{\infty} (f, f_\beta)g_\beta,$$

where $\sum_{\beta=1}^{\infty} |(f, u_\beta)|^2 + \sum_{\beta=1}^{\infty} |(f, f_\beta)|^2$ converges, so that $\mathfrak{A}^*$ is defined in all of $\mathfrak{H}$. Since $\mathfrak{A}$ is also defined in all of $\mathfrak{H}$, $\mathfrak{A}^*$ is bounded; but this implies the boundedness of $\mathfrak{A}$.

§6. Completely Continuous Operators in $\mathfrak{H}$

1. Definition of Complete Continuity

In §5 we showed that if $\mathfrak{K}$ is a bounded linear operator in $\mathfrak{H}$, then $y_n \to y$ always implies that $\mathfrak{K}y_n \to \mathfrak{K}y$. For a weakly convergent sequence $y_n \rightharpoonup y$ we also have $\mathfrak{K}y_n \rightharpoonup \mathfrak{K}y$. If $\mathfrak{K}$ is defined on all of $\mathfrak{H}$, we can consider the very special case when $y_n \rightharpoonup y$ implies $\mathfrak{K}y_n \to \mathfrak{K}y$. In such a case we call $\mathfrak{K}$ a *completely continuous operator* in $\mathfrak{H}$.

Not all bounded operators are completely continuous. For example, the identity operator $\mathfrak{J}$ which associates with every element x in $\mathfrak{H}$ the image x is obviously bounded but not completely continuous, for, as we know, there exist weakly convergent sequences which are not strongly convergent.

On the other hand, *every completely continuous operator is bounded*—for such an operator transforms strongly convergent sequences into strongly convergent sequences and is therefore a continuous and so a bounded operator.

If $\mathfrak{K}$ is completely continuous then, for any two weakly convergent sequences $y_n \rightharpoonup y$ in $\mathfrak{H}$ and $x_m \rightharpoonup x$ in $\mathfrak{H}'$, we always have $(\mathfrak{K}y_n, x_m) \to (\mathfrak{K}y, x)$. *The converse holds provided the domain of definition of $\mathfrak{K}$ is all of $\mathfrak{H}$.*

Indeed, suppose $\mathfrak{K}$ is completely continuous. Then

$$(\mathfrak{K}y_n, x_m) - (\mathfrak{K}y, x) = (\mathfrak{K}(y_n - y), x_m) + (\mathfrak{K}y, x_m - x).$$

The second summand on the right tends to zero while the first summand is bounded in absolute value by the product $\|\mathfrak{K}(y_n - y)\| \cdot \|x_m\|$. In this product the factor $\|x_m\|$ remains bounded while the factor $\mathfrak{K}(y_n - y)$ tends to zero.

To prove the converse, let us put $x_m = x$. Then

$$(\mathfrak{K}y_n, x) \to (\mathfrak{K}y, x).$$

Since x is an arbitrary element of $\mathfrak{H}'$ it follows that $\mathfrak{K}y_n \rightharpoonup \mathfrak{K}y$. If we now put $x_n = \mathfrak{K}y_n - \mathfrak{K}y \rightharpoonup 0$, then we have

$$(\mathfrak{K}(y_n - y), \mathfrak{K}(y_n - y)) \to 0 \qquad \text{as} \quad n \to \infty.$$

This means that $\|\mathfrak{K}(y_n - y)\| \to 0$, which implies the strong convergence $\mathfrak{K}y_n \to \mathfrak{K}y$.

2. *Sufficient Condition for Complete Continuity*

The following condition implies that $\mathfrak{K}$ is completely continuous: *Let $(a_{\alpha\beta}) = (\mathfrak{K}\psi_\beta, \varphi_\alpha)$ be the kernel matrix of a bounded linear operator with respect to the complete orthonormal systems (ψ) in $\mathfrak{H}$ and (φ) in $\mathfrak{H}'$. Then if $\sum_{\alpha,\beta=1}^{\infty} |a_{\alpha\beta}|^2$ converges, $\mathfrak{K}$ must be completely continuous.*

In fact we know that if $y_n \rightharpoonup y$, then

$$(\mathfrak{K}(y_n - y), \varphi_\alpha) = \left(\sum_{\beta=1}^{\infty} \mathfrak{K}\psi_\beta(y_n^{(\beta)} - y^{(\beta)}), \varphi_\alpha \right)$$

$$= \sum_{\beta=1}^{\infty} (y_n^{(\beta)} - y^{(\beta)})(\mathfrak{K}\psi_\beta, \varphi_\alpha) = \sum_{\beta=1}^{\infty} a_{\alpha\beta}(y_n^{(\beta)} - y^{(\beta)}),$$

where $y_n^{(\beta)}$ and $y^{(\beta)}$ are the Fourier coefficients of y_n and y, respectively. Hence

$$\|\mathfrak{K}(y_n - y)\|^2 = \sum_{\alpha=1}^{\infty} \left| \sum_{\beta=1}^{\infty} a_{\alpha\beta}(y_n^{(\beta)} - y^{(\beta)}) \right|^2.$$

It remains to show that this last expression tends to zero as $n \to \infty$. Now

$$\sum_{\alpha=1}^{\infty} \left| \sum_{\beta=1}^{\infty} a_{\alpha\beta}(y_n^{(\beta)} - y^{(\beta)}) \right|^2 = \sum_{\alpha=1}^{m} \left| \sum_{\beta=1}^{\infty} a_{\alpha\beta}(y_n^{(\beta)} - y^{(\beta)}) \right|^2$$

$$+ \sum_{\alpha=m+1}^{\infty} \left| \sum_{\beta=1}^{\infty} a_{\alpha\beta}(y_n^{(\beta)} - y^{(\beta)}) \right|^2.$$

In view of Schwarz's inequality, the second summand on the right is

$$\leqq \sum_{\alpha=m+1}^{\infty} \left(\sum_{\beta=1}^{\infty} |a_{\alpha\beta}|^2 \cdot \sum_{\beta=1}^{\infty} |y_n^{(\beta)} - y^{(\beta)}|^2 \right)$$

$$= \sum_{\alpha=m+1}^{\infty} \sum_{\beta=1}^{\infty} |a_{\alpha\beta}|^2 \cdot \|y_n - y\|^2,$$

where the $\|y_n - y\|$ are bounded. Therefore, as m tends to infinity, the second summand tends to zero uniformly in n. The first summand is

$$= \sum_{\alpha=1}^{m} |(\mathfrak{K}(y_n - y), \varphi_\alpha)|^2.$$

Now, for fixed m, each of the m summands in the last sum tends to zero as $n \to \infty$, because $\mathfrak{K}(y_n - y) \rightharpoonup 0$. This completes the proof.

An integral operator $\mathfrak{K}y = \int_a^b K(s, t)y(t)\,dt$, *having a kernel* $K(s, t)$ *such that*

$$\int_a^b \int_c^d |K(s, t)|^2\,ds\,dt, \qquad \begin{matrix} a \leqq t \leqq b \\ c \leqq s \leqq d \end{matrix}$$

exists, must be a bounded, completely continuous operator.

Let us first note that for each y in $\mathfrak{L}_2(a, b)$

$$\|\mathfrak{K}y\|^2 = \int_c^d \left| \int_a^b K(s, t)y(t)\,dt \right|^2 ds \leqq \int_c^d \int_a^b |K(s, t)|^2\,dt\,ds \|y\|^2,$$

which shows that $\mathfrak{K}$ is bounded and thus $\mathfrak{K}^*$ is well defined in $\mathfrak{H}'$. Moreover,

$$\sum_{\beta=1}^{\infty} |a_{\alpha\beta}|^2 = \sum_{\beta=1}^{\infty} |(\mathfrak{K}\psi_\beta, \varphi_\alpha)|^2 = \sum_{\beta=1}^{\infty} |(\psi_\beta, \mathfrak{K}^*\varphi_\alpha)|^2 = \|\mathfrak{K}^*\varphi_\alpha\|^2$$

$$\begin{aligned}\sum_{\alpha=1}^{m} \sum_{\beta=1}^{\infty} |a_{\alpha\beta}|^2 &= \sum_{\alpha=1}^{m} \int_a^b \left| \int_c^d \overline{K(s, t)\varphi_\alpha(s)}\, ds \right|^2 dt \\ &= \int_a^b \sum_{\alpha=1}^{m} \left| \int_c^d \overline{K(s, t)\varphi_\alpha(s)}\, ds \right|^2 dt \\ &\leqq \int_a^b \sum_{\alpha=1}^{\infty} \left| \int_c^d \overline{K(s, t)\varphi_\alpha(s)}\, ds \right|^2 dt \\ &= \int_a^b \int_c^d |K(s, t)|^2\, ds\, dt.^6\end{aligned}$$

This implies that $\sum_{\alpha,\beta=1}^{\infty} |a_{\alpha\beta}|^2$ must converge. In view of the previous theorem our contention follows.

3. *Schmidt's Normal Form*

Any bounded operator, and hence, in particular, any completely continuous operator, has been represented by means of a kernel matrix. The choice of complete orthonormal systems (φ) and (ψ) in $\mathfrak{H}'$ and $\mathfrak{H}$, respectively, needed to realize this representation is completely arbitrary. In what follows we propose to show how an appropriate choice of orthonormal systems can lead to a kernel matrix of especially simple form, namely, a diagonal matrix.

Let us consider the function $(\mathfrak{K}y, x)$ of two vectors x in $\mathfrak{H}'$ and y in $\mathfrak{H}$. We shall call this function completely continuous (in two variables) inasmuch as $x_m \rightharpoonup x$ and $y_n \rightharpoonup y$ imply that $(\mathfrak{K}y_n, x_m) \to (\mathfrak{K}y, x)$.

[6] Since $\int_c^d |K(s, t)|^2\, ds$ exists, $K(s, t)$ is in $\mathfrak{L}_2(c, d)$ for each t in (a, b). Hence $\int_c^d |K(s, t)|^2\, ds = \|K(s, t)\|^2 = \sum_{\alpha=1}^{\infty} |\int_c^d K(s, t)\varphi_\alpha(s)\, ds|^2$. (Ed.)

Let us now consider the equations

$$\mathfrak{K}y_0 = 0, \qquad \mathfrak{K}^*x_0 = 0.$$

The solutions y_0 of $\mathfrak{K}y_0 = 0$ form a subspace of $\mathfrak{H}$ known as the (direct) kernel of $\mathfrak{K}$ and the solutions x_0 of $\mathfrak{K}^*x_0 = 0$ form a subspace of $\mathfrak{H}'$ known as the adjoint kernel of $\mathfrak{K}$ (or the (direct) kernel of $\mathfrak{K}^*$). The kernel of $\mathfrak{K}$ is also called the null space of $\mathfrak{K}$. In both cases these spaces can be generated by complete orthonormal systems (ψ_0) and (φ_0), where (ψ_0) generates the space of the y_0 and (φ_0) generates the space of the x_0. Note that since $(\mathfrak{K}y, x) = (y, \mathfrak{K}^*x)$, $\mathfrak{K} = 0$ if and only if $\mathfrak{K}^* = 0$. Hence if we rule out $\mathfrak{K} = 0$, then (ψ_0) is not complete in $\mathfrak{H}$ and (φ_0) is not complete in $\mathfrak{H}'$.

The function $|(\mathfrak{K}y, x)|^2$, where x and y satisfy the side conditions $\|x\| \leqq 1$ and $\|y\| \leqq 1$, attains a maximum M at a point x_1, y_1. To prove this contention, let M denote the least upper bound of the totality of values of $|(\mathfrak{K}y, x)|^2$. M always exists, for $|(\mathfrak{K}y, x)|^2 \leqq \|\mathfrak{K}\|^2 \cdot \|x\|^2 \cdot \|y\|^2 \leqq \|\mathfrak{K}\|^2$. Hence we can find a sequence $x^{(n)}$, $y^{(n)}$ $(n = 1, 2, \cdots)$ such that $|(\mathfrak{K}y^{(n)}, x^{(n)})|^2$ tends to M as a limit, while $\|x^{(n)}\|$ and $\|y^{(n)}\|$ remain $\leqq 1$. By a result of §3 (cf. p. 24) we can extract from this sequence a weakly convergent subsequence $x^{(n_\alpha)}$ and $y^{(m_\beta)}$ such that $|(\mathfrak{K}y^{(m_\beta)}, x^{(n_\alpha)})|^2$ converges to M. Let the limit of this convergent subsequence be x_1 in $\mathfrak{H}'$ and y_1 in $\mathfrak{H}$. Then $|(\mathfrak{K}y_1, x_1)|^2 = M$. We further contend that $\|x_1\| = \|y_1\| = 1$, for otherwise we would have

$$\left|\left(\mathfrak{K}\frac{y_1}{\|y_1\|}, \frac{x_1}{\|x_1\|}\right)\right|^2 = \frac{M}{\|x_1\|^2\|y_1\|^2} > M,$$

which is impossible. If we added an arbitrary element of the adjoint kernel of $\mathfrak{K}$ to x_1 or an arbitrary element of the kernel of $\mathfrak{K}$ to y_1, then the value of $|(\mathfrak{K}y_1, x_1)|$ would remain unchanged We can therefore assume x_1 to be orthogonal to all the φ_0 and y_1 orthogonal to all the ψ_0 and still have $|(\mathfrak{K}y_1, x_1)|^2 = M$. Let us put $(\mathfrak{K}y_1, x_1) = \kappa_1 + i\kappa_2 = \kappa \neq 0$. Then $M = \kappa_1{}^2 + \kappa_2{}^2$. Now let x^* be an element orthogonal to x_1 (and all the φ_0) such that $\|x^*\| = 1$. We claim that $(\mathfrak{K}y_1, x^*) = (y_1, \mathfrak{K}^*x^*) = 0$.

In fact, suppose $(\mathfrak{K}y_1, x^*) = \mu = \mu_1 + i\mu_2$. We then have for constants c_1, c_2:

$$(\mathfrak{K}y_1, \bar{c}_1 x_1 + \bar{c}_2 x^*) = c_1 \kappa + c_2 \mu.$$

If we impose the condition $\|c_1 x_1 + c_2 x^*\| = 1$, then the Hermitian form $|c_1 \kappa + c_2 \mu|^2$, subject to the side condition $|c_1|^2 + |c_2|^2 = 1$, takes on the maximum $|\kappa|^2 = M$. This means that M is an eigenvalue of this form. Now a little calculation shows that $\mu = 0$.

Similarly, we can show that for any element y^* orthogonal to y_1 (and all the ψ_0) we must have $(\mathfrak{K}y^*, x_1) = (y^*, \mathfrak{K}^* x_1) = 0$.

We now put $\mathfrak{K}y_1 - \kappa x_1 = x$. Then, for each φ_0 we have $(x, \varphi_0) = (\mathfrak{K}y_1, \varphi_0) - \kappa(x_1, \varphi_0) = (y_1, \mathfrak{K}^*\varphi_0) = 0$. Furthermore, $(x, x_1) = (\mathfrak{K}y_1, x_1) - \kappa(x_1, x_1) = \kappa - \kappa = 0$. For each x^* we also have $(x, x^*) = (\mathfrak{K}y_1, x^*) - \kappa(x_1, x^*) = 0$. Therefore x is orthogonal to all the elements of a complete orthonormal system in $\mathfrak{H}'$ obtainable by extension from (φ_0) and x_1. This means that $x = 0$. Consequently,

$$\mathfrak{K}y_1 = \kappa x_1 \qquad (\|x_1\| = \|y_1\| = 1).$$

In exactly the same way we can show that

$$\mathfrak{K}^* x_1 = \bar{\kappa} y_1.$$

We shall call κ a normal value of the operator $\mathfrak{K}$. The only restriction on κ is that $|\kappa|^2 = M$. Since multiplication of our equations by a factor of length one does not violate this restriction or the restrictions $\|x_1\| = 1$, $\|y_1\| = 1$, we may assume that y_1 and x_1 have been chosen to begin with so that the normal value associated with them is $\kappa_1 = |\kappa| > 0$. Thus

$$\begin{aligned} \mathfrak{K}y_1 &= \kappa_1 x_1 \\ \mathfrak{K}^* x_1 &= \kappa_1 y_1 \end{aligned} \qquad (\kappa_1 > 0, \quad \|x_1\| = \|y_1\| = 1).$$

We can now continue the procedure we used above, to find the maximum of $|(\mathfrak{K}y, x)|^2$ under the side conditions $\|x\| \leqq 1$, $\|y\| \leqq 1$, where we further restrict x to be orthogonal in $\mathfrak{H}'$ to

(φ_0) and x_1 while y is restricted to be orthogonal in $\mathfrak{H}$ to (ψ_0) and y_1. We are thereby led to a system of equations

$$\begin{aligned} \mathfrak{K}y_2 &= \kappa_2 x_2 \\ \mathfrak{K}^* x_2 &= \kappa_2 y_2 \end{aligned} \qquad (0 < \kappa_2 \leqq \kappa_1, \quad \|x_2\| = \|y_2\| = 1),$$

and so forth. In general, suppose $x_1, \cdots, x_{n-1}$ and $y_1, \cdots, y_{n-1}$ have already been determined. We then seek the maximum of $|(\mathfrak{K}y, x)|^2$ under the conditions $\|x\| \leqq 1$, $\|y\| \leqq 1$, where we further restrict x to be orthogonal in $\mathfrak{H}'$ to (φ_0) and $x_1, \cdots, x_{n-1}$ while y is restricted to be orthogonal in $\mathfrak{H}$ to (ψ_0) and $y_1, \cdots y_{n-1}$. This now leads us to the system of equations

$$\begin{aligned} \mathfrak{K}y_n &= \kappa_n x_n \\ \mathfrak{K}^* x_n &= \kappa_n y_n \end{aligned} \qquad (0 < \kappa_n \leqq \cdots \leqq \kappa_1, \quad \|x_n\| = \|y_n\| = 1).$$

The above procedure can be iterated until one obtains a complete orthonormal system. This may require a finite or denumerably infinite number of steps. If the system (φ_0), $x_1, \cdots$, x_n turns out to be a complete orthonormal system, then (ψ_0), $y_1, \cdots, y_n$ must also be a complete orthonormal system, for if an element y in $\mathfrak{H}$ is orthogonal to (ψ_0), $y_1, \cdots, y_n$, then, because $(y_\alpha, y) = 0$, we must have $(y, \mathfrak{K}^* x_\alpha) = (\mathfrak{K}y, x_\alpha) = 0$ and $(y, \mathfrak{K}^* \varphi_0) = (\mathfrak{K}y, \varphi_0) = 0$. Hence $\mathfrak{K}y$ is orthogonal to (φ_0), $x_1, \cdots, x_n$, which means that $\mathfrak{K}y = 0$, i.e., y belongs to the kernel of $\mathfrak{K}$. On the other hand, y is orthogonal to all (ψ_0), which means that $y = 0$. In such a case we call the operator $\mathfrak{K}$ degenerate. If $\mathfrak{K}$ is degenerate, then for each y in $\mathfrak{H}$ we have the representation

$$y = b_1 y_1 + \cdots + b_n y_n + \psi_0 \qquad (b_\alpha = (y, y_\alpha)),$$

while, on the other hand

$$\begin{aligned} \mathfrak{K}y &= b_1 \kappa_1 x_1 + \cdots + b_n \kappa_n x_n \\ x &= a_1 x_1 + \cdots + a_n x_n + \varphi_0 \end{aligned} \qquad (a_\alpha = (x, x_\alpha)).$$

If, in this case, we take the systems (ψ_0), $y_1, \cdots, y_n$ and (φ_0), $x_1, \cdots, x_n$ as fundamental sets, or bases, then the associated kernel matrix has as its principal diagonal entries, apart from zeros, only the elements $\kappa_1, \cdots, \kappa_n$.

In the nondegenerate, or general case, it takes a denumerable infinity of iterations to attain the complete orthonormal systems (ψ_0), $y_1, y_2, \cdots$ and (φ_0), $x_1, x_2, \cdots$. These systems are often called the Schmidt orthonormal systems of the operator $\mathfrak{K}$. In this case we have the representations

$$y = b_1 y_1 + b_2 y_2 + \cdots + \psi_0$$

$$\mathfrak{K}y = b_1 \kappa_1 x_1 + b_2 \kappa_2 x_2 + \cdots \qquad (b_\alpha = (y, y_\alpha))$$

$$x = a_1 x_1 + a_2 x_2 + \cdots + \varphi_0$$

$$(\mathfrak{K}y, x) = \overline{a_1} b_1 \kappa_1 + \overline{a_2} b_2 \kappa_2 + \cdots \qquad (a_\alpha = (x, x_\alpha)).$$

This representation of $\mathfrak{K}y$ is frequently called the "expansion formula," while the expression for $(\mathfrak{K}y, x)$ is known as the "fundamental formula."

The kernel matrix of $\mathfrak{K}$ with respect to the above orthonormal systems is essentially a diagonal matrix with diagonal elements $\kappa_1, \kappa_2, \cdots$ (apart from rows and columns of zeros corresponding, respectively, to the adjoint kernel and kernel of $\mathfrak{K}$).

Furthermore, since $(\mathfrak{K}y_n, x_n) = \kappa_n$, it follows from the complete continuity of $\mathfrak{K}$ that if $y_n \rightharpoonup 0$ and $x_n \rightharpoonup 0$, then $\kappa_n \to 0$ as $n \to \infty$. *The sequence of normal values converges to the limit* 0. This means that each of the normal values can only appear in the above sequence a finite number of times. Hence *the number of distinct couples* x_n, y_n *such that* $(\mathfrak{K}y_n, x_n) = \kappa_n$ *must be finite.*

We can use the Schmidt orthonormal systems to solve the first type of operator equation

$$\mathfrak{K}y = x,$$

where x is given. In order for a solution to exist, we must first have $(x, \varphi_0) = 0$, i.e., *the right side of the above equation must be orthogonal to all elements in the adjoint kernel of* $\mathfrak{K}$—for we must have $(x, \varphi_0) = (\mathfrak{K}y, \varphi_0) = (y, \mathfrak{K}^*\varphi_0) = 0$.

In addition, the previous formulas imply directly that

$$b_\alpha \kappa_\alpha = a_\alpha; \qquad b_\alpha = \frac{a_\alpha}{\kappa_\alpha}, \qquad (y, y_\alpha) = \frac{(x, x_\alpha)}{\kappa_\alpha}.$$

Hence *a necessary condition for the existence of a solution of our operator equation is that* $\sum_{\alpha=1}^{\infty}|(x, x_\alpha)|^2/\kappa_\alpha{}^2$ *converge. If, in addition, x is orthogonal to all elements in the adjoint kernel of* $\mathfrak{K}$, *then our operator equation always admits a solution.* In this case

$$y = \sum_{\alpha=1}^{\infty} \frac{(x, x_\alpha)}{\kappa_\alpha} y_\alpha$$

is an element of $\mathfrak{H}$ and, at the same time, a solution of smallest possible norm; the most general solution is $y = \sum_{\alpha=1}^{\infty} [(x, x_\alpha)/\kappa_\alpha]/y_\alpha + \psi_0$.

§7. The Fredholm Theorems for Completely Continuous Operators

1. The Alternative Theorem

In what follows we shall always assume that $\mathfrak{H}' = \mathfrak{H}$ and that $\mathfrak{K}$ is a completely continuous operator. The operator equation of the second kind then reads

$$y + \mathfrak{K}y = x.$$

In studying this equation we again assume that we are employing the Schmidt orthonormal systems. Let x be of the form

$$x = \sum_{(\alpha)} a_\alpha x_\alpha + \sum_{(\nu)} b_\nu \varphi_\nu,$$

where the φ_ν belong to the adjoint kernel of $\mathfrak{K}$ (direct kernel of $\mathfrak{K}^*$). Let us put $(y, x_\alpha) = \xi_\alpha$ and $(y, \varphi_\nu) = \eta_\nu$. Then

$$a_\alpha = \xi_\alpha + (\mathfrak{K}y, x_\alpha) = \xi_\alpha + (y, \mathfrak{K}^* x_\alpha) = \xi_\alpha + (y, \kappa_\alpha y_\alpha)$$

$$= \xi_\alpha + \kappa_\alpha \left[\sum_{(\beta)} (x_\beta, y_\alpha)\xi_\beta + \sum_{(\nu)} (\varphi_\nu, y_\alpha)\eta_\nu\right] \qquad (\alpha = 1, 2, \cdots),$$

$$b_\nu = (y + \mathfrak{K}y, \varphi_\nu) = \eta_\nu + (\mathfrak{K}y, \varphi_\nu) = \eta_\nu + (y, \mathfrak{K}^*\varphi_\nu) = \eta_\nu \qquad (\nu = 1, 2, \cdots),$$

or

$$\xi_\alpha + \kappa_\alpha \sum_{(\beta)} (x_\beta, y_\alpha)\xi_\beta = a_\alpha - \kappa_\alpha \sum_{(\nu)} (\varphi_\nu, y_\alpha) b_\nu = c_\alpha \quad (\alpha = 1, 2, \cdots).$$

If the kernel of $\mathfrak{K}$ is degenerate, our system reduces to a finite number of equations. The theorems governing this case are well known. As for the infinite case, let us first consider solving the "residue system" of equations:

$$\xi_\alpha + \kappa_\alpha \sum_{\beta=N}^{\infty} (x_\beta, y_\alpha)\xi_\beta = c_\alpha - \kappa_\alpha \sum_{\beta=1}^{N-1} (x_\beta, y_\alpha)\xi_\beta \qquad (\alpha = N, N+1, \cdots).$$

We shall show that this system can be solved for $\xi_N, \xi_{N+1}, \cdots$ *for* N *sufficiently large*. If we substitute this solution into the original system we are again left with a finite system of $N-1$ equations in the unknowns $\xi_1, \cdots, \xi_{N-1}$. In order to show that the residue system can be solved we proceed as follows: Denote by $\mathfrak{A} = \mathfrak{A}(N)$ the kernel matrix $(a_{\alpha\beta})$, with $a_{\alpha\beta} = (\mathfrak{K}x_\beta, x_\alpha) = (x_\beta, \mathfrak{K}^* x_\alpha) = (x_\beta, \kappa_\alpha y_\alpha)$, $\alpha, \beta = N, N+1, \cdots$. Since

$$\left|\sum_{\alpha=N}^{\infty}\left(\sum_{\beta=N}^{\infty} z_\beta (x_\beta, \kappa_\alpha y_\alpha) t_\alpha\right)\right| = \left|\left(\sum_{\beta=N}^{\infty} x_\beta z_\beta, \sum_{\alpha=N}^{\infty} \kappa_\alpha y_\alpha t_\alpha\right)\right|$$
$$\leqq \sqrt{\sum_{\beta=N}^{\infty} |z_\beta|^2 \cdot \sum_{\alpha=N}^{\infty} \kappa_\alpha^2 |t_\alpha|^2},$$

the norm $\|\mathfrak{A}\|$ of $\mathfrak{A}$, i.e., the norm of the function defined by $\mathfrak{A}$, tends to zero for arbitrary z_β and t_α with $\sum_{\beta=1}^{\infty} |z_\beta|^2 < \infty$ and $\sum_{\alpha=1}^{\infty} |t_\alpha|^2 < \infty$ (this because $\kappa_\alpha \to 0$). If we choose N so large that $\|\mathfrak{A}\| < 1$, then the matrix sum $\mathfrak{E} - \mathfrak{A} + \mathfrak{A}^2 - \cdots + (-1)^k \mathfrak{A}^k$ tends to a limit as $k \to \infty$.[7] This limit represents a bounded matrix $\mathfrak{R} = (r_{\alpha\beta})$ with $\|\mathfrak{R}\| \leqq 1/(1 - \|\mathfrak{A}\|)$ and

$$(\mathfrak{E} + \mathfrak{A})\mathfrak{R} = \mathfrak{R}(\mathfrak{E} + \mathfrak{A}) = \mathfrak{E}.$$

[7] Let $\mathfrak{B}_n$ be a sequence of bounded operators on $\mathfrak{H}$ and let $\mathfrak{B}$ be a bounded operator on $\mathfrak{H}$. To say that $\mathfrak{B}_n \to \mathfrak{B}$ means that $\mathfrak{B}_n y \to \mathfrak{B} y$ for all y in $\mathfrak{H}$. Equivalently, $\mathfrak{B}_n \to \mathfrak{B}$ means that $\|\mathfrak{B}_n\| \to \|\mathfrak{B}\|$. The following basic theorem holds: If $\mathfrak{C}_n$ is a Cauchy sequence of bounded operators on $\mathfrak{H}$ (that is, if $\|\mathfrak{C}_n - \mathfrak{C}_m\| \to 0$ as $n, m \to \infty$), then there exists a unique bounded operator $\mathfrak{C}$ on $\mathfrak{H}$ such that $\mathfrak{C}_n \to \mathfrak{C}$. (Ed.)

Consequently, the solution to the residue system is

$$\xi_\alpha = \sum_{\beta=N}^{\infty} r_{\alpha\beta}\left(c_\beta - \kappa_\beta \sum_{\gamma=1}^{N-1} (x_\gamma, y_\beta)\xi_\gamma\right) = k_\alpha + \sum_{\gamma=1}^{N-1} l_{\alpha\gamma}\xi_\gamma$$

$$(\alpha = N, N+1 \ldots)$$

$$k_\alpha = \sum_{\beta=N}^{\infty} r_{\alpha\beta} c_\beta, \; l_{\alpha\gamma} = -\sum_{\beta=N}^{\infty} r_{\alpha\beta}\kappa_\beta (x_\gamma, y_\beta).$$

If we substitute this solution into our first system of equations we obtain the following finite system:

$$\xi_\alpha + \kappa_\alpha \sum_{\beta=1}^{N-1} (x_\beta, y_\alpha)\xi_\beta + \kappa_\alpha \sum_{\beta=N}^{\infty} (x_\beta, y_\alpha)\left(k_\beta + \sum_{\gamma=1}^{N-1} l_{\beta\gamma}\xi_\gamma\right) = c_\alpha$$

$$(\alpha = 1, \cdots, N-1)$$

$$\xi_\alpha + \kappa_\alpha \sum_{\beta=1}^{N-1}\left[(x_\beta, y_\alpha) + \sum_{\mu=N}^{\infty} (x_\mu, y_\alpha) l_{\mu\beta}\right]\xi_\beta = c_\alpha - \kappa_\alpha \sum_{\beta=N}^{\infty} (x_\beta, y_\alpha) k_\beta.$$

We must now distinguish between two cases: The determinant of our system is equal to zero or it is different from zero. Suppose the determinant is different from zero. Then our system possesses a unique solution $\xi_1, \cdots, \xi_{N-1}$ which, combined with the solution of the residue system, gives us a square summable solution $\xi_1, \xi_2, \cdots$ of our original system and so a unique solution of our original operator equation. Now suppose the determinant in question is equal to zero, and let us examine the homogeneous operator equation $y + \mathfrak{K}y = 0$. We then have $a_\alpha = 0$, $b_\nu = 0$, $c_\alpha = 0$, $k_\alpha = 0$ and hence our finite system in $\xi_1, \cdots, \xi_{N-1}$ must also be homogeneous and must admit a nontrivial solution; to be more precise, a finite number of linearly independent solutions. Every such solution leads, with the aid of the residue system, to a solution of our homogeneous system, and so, to a solution of the associated operator equation. Thus there must exist a finite number of linearly independent solutions to our homogeneous operator equation.

Fredholm's First Theorem.[8] *Let $\mathfrak{K}$ be a completely continuous operator on $\mathfrak{H}$. Then either the equation $y + \mathfrak{K}y = x$ has a unique solution y for every x in $\mathfrak{H}$, or else the homogeneous equation $y + \mathfrak{K}y = 0$ has a finite number of linearly independent solutions.*

2. *Adjoint Equations*

We shall now turn our attention to the adjoint operator $\mathfrak{K}^*$ and examine the equation

$$y + \mathfrak{K}^*y = x.$$

Keeping the same complete orthonormal system x_α, φ_ν and the same notations as before, we have

$$\begin{aligned}
a_\alpha = (y + \mathfrak{K}^*y, x_\alpha) &= \xi_\alpha + (y, \mathfrak{K}x_\alpha) \\
&= \xi_\alpha + \sum_{(\beta)} (x_\beta, \mathfrak{K}x_\alpha)\xi_\beta + \sum_{(\nu)} (\varphi_\nu, \mathfrak{K}x_\alpha)\eta_\nu \\
&= \xi_\alpha + \sum_{(\beta)} (\mathfrak{K}^*x_\beta, x_\alpha)\xi_\beta = \xi_\alpha + \sum_{(\beta)} (\kappa_\beta y_\beta, x_\alpha)\xi_\beta \qquad (\alpha = 1, 2, \cdots),
\end{aligned}$$

$$\begin{aligned}
b_\nu = (y + \mathfrak{K}^*y, \varphi_\nu) &= \eta_\nu + \sum_{(\beta)} (x_\beta, \mathfrak{K}\varphi_\nu)\xi_\beta \\
&= \eta_\nu + \sum_{(\beta)} (\kappa_\beta y_\beta, \varphi_\nu)\xi_\beta \qquad (\nu = 1, 2, \cdots).
\end{aligned}$$

Hence our residue system of equations is

$$\xi_\alpha + \sum_{\beta=N}^{\infty} (\kappa_\beta y_\beta, x_\alpha)\xi_\beta = a_\alpha - \sum_{\beta=1}^{N-1} (\kappa_\beta y_\beta, x_\alpha)\xi_\beta \qquad (\alpha = N, N+1, \cdots).$$

Now the matrix of this system is precisely $\mathfrak{A}^*$; hence $(\mathfrak{E} + \mathfrak{A}^*)\mathfrak{R}^* = \mathfrak{R}^*(\mathfrak{E} + \mathfrak{A}^*) = \mathfrak{E}$ and

$$\xi_\alpha = \sum_{\beta=N}^{\infty} \bar{r}_{\beta\alpha}\left(a_\beta - \sum_{\gamma=1}^{N-1} (\kappa_\gamma y_\gamma, x_\beta)\xi_\gamma\right) \qquad (\alpha = N, N+1, \cdots).$$

[8] Fredholm proved these theorems for integral equations with continuous kernel. The generalization to completely continuous operators is due to Hilbert.

Substituting these values into our original equations gives

$$\xi_\alpha + \sum_{\beta=1}^{N-1} \left[(\kappa_\beta y_\beta, x_\alpha) - \sum_{\gamma,\mu=N}^{\infty} (\kappa_\mu y_\mu, x_\alpha) \bar{r}_{\gamma\mu} (\kappa_\beta y_\beta, x_\gamma) \right] \xi_\beta = \text{const.}$$

$$(\alpha = 1, \cdots, N-1).$$

If we compare this system to that encountered in our previous problem, we see that they differ only in the fact that now our matrix is the conjugate transpose of the previous matrix. The following result must therefore hold:

Fredholm's Second Theorem. *For the adjoint operator there arise two mutually exclusive possibilities: either $y + \mathfrak{K}y = x$ and $y + \mathfrak{K}^*y = z$ both admit unique solutions for any x and z, or else both homogeneous equations $y + \mathfrak{K}y = 0$ and $y + \mathfrak{K}^*y = 0$ admit the same finite number of linearly independent solutions* (cf. Fredholm's First Theorem).

This last statement follows immediately from the fact that the number of independent solutions of the operator equation is the same as the number of independent solutions of the finite system of equations. This last number is the same for both equations, for in each case the associated finite matrices are of the same rank.

We now establish

Fredholm's Third Theorem. *A necessary and sufficient condition for the equation $y + \mathfrak{K}y = x$ to have a solution is that x be orthogonal to all the solutions y_0 of the equation $y_0 + \mathfrak{K}^*y_0 = 0$.*[9]

Proof. Let M be the null space of $\mathfrak{I} + \mathfrak{K}^*$ and let $M^\perp$ be the orthogonal complement of M. Then $\mathfrak{H} = M \oplus M^\perp$. Let R be the range of $\mathfrak{I} + \mathfrak{K}$. We shall prove later that R is closed. For x in R and φ in M we have $(x, \varphi) = ((\mathfrak{I} + \mathfrak{K})y, \varphi) = 0$.

[9] The author's proof of sufficiency is very brief. The proof given here is a somewhat modified version of the proof found in Akhiezer and Glazman (see the bibliography on p. 120). (Ed.)

Hence $R \subset M^{\perp}$. On the other hand, if f is in $R^{\perp}$ and h is in $\mathfrak{H}$, then $(h, (\mathfrak{I} + \mathfrak{K}^*)f) = ((\mathfrak{I} + \mathfrak{K})h, f) = 0$. This shows that f belongs to M, so that $R^{\perp} \subset M$. In view of the (still unproved) closedness of R, $R^{\perp} \subset M$ is equivalent to $R \supset M^{\perp}$. Together, $R \subset M^{\perp}$ and $R \supset M^{\perp}$ yield the required conclusion: $R = M^{\perp}$.

It remains to prove the assumed closedness of the range R of $\mathfrak{I} + \mathfrak{K}$. This is an easy consequence of an interesting result which we are about to state and prove. Thus let $\mathfrak{T}$ be a linear operator on $\mathfrak{H}$ with null space N and range R. Then $\mathfrak{T}$ effects a one-to-one mapping of $N^{\perp}$, the orthogonal complement of N, onto R. We shall show that *if* $\mathfrak{T} = \mathfrak{I} + \mathfrak{K}$, $\mathfrak{K}$ *completely continuous, then the inverse mapping* $\mathfrak{T}^{-1}$ *with domain of definition* R *and range* $N^{\perp}$ *is bounded.*

Proof. If $\mathfrak{T}^{-1}$ is not bounded, then we can find a sequence $x_n = \mathfrak{T}y_n$ such that $\|x_n\| \leqq m$ and $\|y_n\| \to \infty$. Now $\mathfrak{T}y_n = (\mathfrak{I} + \mathfrak{K})y_n = x_n$ implies that

$$\frac{y_n}{\|y_n\|} + \mathfrak{K}\frac{y_n}{\|y_n\|} = \frac{x_n}{\|y_n\|} \to 0.$$

The vectors $y_n/\|y_n\|$ are a sequence of unit vectors. As such they must contain a weakly convergent subsequence which we may take to be the original sequence. Thus, $y_n/\|y_n\| \rightharpoonup y$. Since $\mathfrak{K}$ is completely continuous, $\mathfrak{K}(y_n/\|y_n\|) \to \mathfrak{K}y$. This means that $y_n/\|y_n\| \to -\mathfrak{K}y$, so that $\mathfrak{K}y = -y$. The last equality states that y is in the null space of $\mathfrak{T} = \mathfrak{I} + \mathfrak{K}$. However, this is impossible because $y \neq 0$ (as the limit of a sequence of vectors of length one) and because $y \perp N$ (as the limit of a sequence of vectors each of which is $\perp N$). This contradiction proves the asserted boundedness of $\mathfrak{T}^{-1}$.

Corollary. *The range* R *of* $\mathfrak{T} = \mathfrak{I} + \mathfrak{K}$ *is closed in* $\mathfrak{H}$. Indeed, let $x_n \to x$, x_n in R. In view of the boundedness of $\mathfrak{T}^{-1}$, $\mathfrak{T}^{-1}x_n \to \mathfrak{T}^{-1}x$. Since $N^{\perp}$ is a closed subspace of $\mathfrak{H}$ and the vectors $\mathfrak{T}^{-1}x_n$ belong to $N^{\perp}$, the same is true of $\mathfrak{T}^{-1}x$. As $\mathfrak{T}$ effects a one-to-one mapping of $N^{\perp}$ onto R, we conclude that $x = \mathfrak{T}(\mathfrak{T}^{-1}x)$ belongs to R. This proves that the range of $\mathfrak{T}$ is closed.

§8. Self-Adjoint and Normal Completely Continuous Operators

1. Eigenvalues and Eigenvectors of Self-Adjoint Operators

If $\mathfrak{H}' = \mathfrak{H}$ and $\mathfrak{K}$ is a bounded operator such that $\mathfrak{K} = \mathfrak{K}^*$, then we say that $\mathfrak{K}$ is *self-adjoint* or *Hermitian*. (We shall use the terms self-adjoint and Hermitian interchangeably.) In what follows we shall again limit ourselves to nonzero completely continuous operators. For a self-adjoint integral operator with kernel $K(s, t)$ we have $\overline{K(t, s)} = K(s, t)$; hence if this kernel is real it must also be symmetric, i.e., $K(t, s) = K(s, t)$ The function $(\mathfrak{K}y, y) = (y, \mathfrak{K}^*y) = \overline{(y, \mathfrak{K}y)}$ is always real valued. If $\|y\| \leqq 1$, then $|(\mathfrak{K}y, y)|$ is bounded and takes on its maximum value at a point y_1. The proof is similar to that in III, §6. Observe that $\|y_1\|$ is necessarily one. We can choose y_1 orthogonal to all y_0 satisfying $\mathfrak{K}y_0 = 0$. The set of all such y_0 spans a subspace which we denote by (y_0). Every element y^* orthogonal to both y_1 and the subspace (y_0) must satisfy the relation $(\mathfrak{K}y_1, y^*) = 0$. Indeed, suppose that $(\mathfrak{K}y_1, y^*) = \mu$. Let M be the maximum of the absolute value of the Hermitian form in c_1, c_2: $(\mathfrak{K}(c_1y_1 + c_2y^*), c_1y_1 + c_2y^*)$ with $|c_1|^2 + |c_2|^2 = 1$. Then M or $-M$ is an eigenvalue of this form. It follows readily that $\mu = (\mathfrak{K}y_1, y^*) = 0$.

Let us suppose $+M$ is an eigenvalue and let us put $\mathfrak{K}y_1 - My_1 = y$. Then $(y, y_0) = 0$ and $(y, y_1) = (\mathfrak{K}y_1, y_1) - M(y_1, y_1) = M - M = 0$. For any y^* orthogonal to (y_0) and y_1 we have

$$(y, y^*) = (\mathfrak{K}y_1, y^*) - M(y_1, y^*) = 0.$$

Hence $y = 0$, i.e., $\mathfrak{K}y_1 = My_1$. If $-M$ is an eigenvalue we obtain in this way the relation $\mathfrak{K}y_1 = -My_1$. Since M cannot equal zero, we may put $\pm M = 1/\lambda_1$. Then

$$\lambda_1\mathfrak{K}y_1 = y_1 \qquad \|y_1\| = 1.$$

We call λ_1 an eigenvalue of $\mathfrak{K}$ and y_1 the associated eigenvector. $\mathfrak{K}$ always possesses at least one eigenvalue.

Let us now seek the maximum of $|(\mathfrak{K}y, y)|$ under the side condition $\|y\| \leqq 1$ for y in $\mathfrak{H}$ orthogonal to (y_0) and y_1. We can then find another eigenvalue λ_2 such that $|\lambda_2| \geqq |\lambda_1|$ (λ_2 can equal λ_1) for which

$$\lambda_2 \mathfrak{K} y_2 = y_2, \qquad \|y_2\| = 1, \qquad (y_1, y_2) = 0.$$

This procedure can be repeated until $y_1, y_2, \cdots, (y_0)$ contain a complete orthonormal system in $\mathfrak{H}$. We then have for all n,

$$\lambda_n \mathfrak{K} y_n = y_n \qquad (|\lambda_1| \leqq |\lambda_2| \leqq \cdots).$$

For every y we then have the representation

$$y = a_1 y_1 + a_2 y_2 + \cdots + y_0$$

$$\mathfrak{K} y = \frac{a_1 y_1}{\lambda_1} + \frac{a_2 y_2}{\lambda_2} + \cdots \qquad \text{(expansion formula)}$$

$$(\mathfrak{K} y, y) = \frac{|a_1|^2}{\lambda_1} + \frac{|a_2|^2}{\lambda_2} + \cdots \qquad \text{(fundamental formula).}$$

It is possible for the sequence $y_1, y_2, \cdots$ to break off; if this happens we call $\mathfrak{K}$ a *degenerate* operator.

From the condition of complete continuity it further follows that $(\mathfrak{K} y_n, y_n) = 1/\lambda_n \to 0$ as $n \to \infty$, i.e., $|\lambda_n| \to \infty$. This means that the set of eigenvalues cannot have a finite point of accumulation.

In sum, we have established the following theorem:

Every completely continuous self-adjoint operator not identically zero possesses a finite or infinite number of real eigenvalues λ_n each with a finite multiplicity. The λ_n have no finite point of accumulation. The associated eigenvectors y_n form an orthonormal system. This orthonormal system can be extended to a complete orthonormal system in $\mathfrak{H}$ by the addition of an orthonormal system of null solutions. The "expansion formula" holds for $\mathfrak{K}y$; the "fundamental formula," for $(\mathfrak{K}y, y)$.

We leave it to the reader to prove the following application of the above theorem:

Suppose $\mathfrak{K} = \mathfrak{K}^*$. If λ is not an eigenvalue of $\mathfrak{K}$, then the operator equation $y - \lambda\mathfrak{K}y = x$ possesses the unique solution

$$y = \sum_{\alpha} \frac{\lambda_\alpha \cdot (x, y_\alpha)}{\lambda_\alpha - \lambda} \cdot y_\alpha + \sum_{\nu} (x, \varphi_\nu)\varphi_\nu, \qquad (\varphi_\nu) = (y_0).$$

However, if λ equals an eigenvalue λ_α and if $(x, y_\alpha) = 0$ for all associated eigenvectors (their number is finite), then

$$y = \sum_{\lambda_\beta \neq \lambda_\alpha} \frac{\lambda_\beta (x, y_\beta)}{\lambda_\beta - \lambda} \cdot y_\beta + \sum_{(\nu)} (x, \varphi_\nu)\varphi_\nu + \sum_{(\alpha)} w_\alpha y_\alpha$$

(w_α are arbitrary constants, y_α are the eigenvectors associated with λ_α).

2. *Normal Operators*

We shall now examine the so-called normal operator, a generalization of the notion of self-adjoint operator. Operators satisfying the relation $\mathfrak{K}\mathfrak{K}^* = \mathfrak{K}^*\mathfrak{K}$ are said to be normal. Let us once again assume that $\mathfrak{H}' = \mathfrak{H}$. Clearly, all self-adjoint operators are normal. We shall soon see that the converse does not hold.

In what follows we assume that $\mathfrak{K}$ is bounded but not necessarily completely continuous. In order to bring out the connection between normal and self-adjoint operators, we define for any bounded operator $\mathfrak{K}$ its two self-adjoint components, namely,

$$\mathfrak{M} = \tfrac{1}{2}(\mathfrak{K} + \mathfrak{K}^*), \qquad \mathfrak{N} = \frac{1}{2i}(\mathfrak{K} - \mathfrak{K}^*).$$

It follows that $\mathfrak{M} = \mathfrak{M}^*$, $\mathfrak{N} = \mathfrak{N}^*$, $\mathfrak{K} = \mathfrak{M} + i\mathfrak{N}$, $\mathfrak{K}^* = \mathfrak{M} - i\mathfrak{N}$. The decomposition $\mathfrak{K} = \mathfrak{M} + i\mathfrak{N}$ is unique; for if we had a second decomposition $\mathfrak{K} = \mathfrak{M}_1 + i\mathfrak{N}_1$ with $\mathfrak{M}_1 = \mathfrak{M}_1{}^*$ and $\mathfrak{N}_1 = \mathfrak{N}_1{}^*$ then

$$\mathfrak{M} - \mathfrak{M}_1 + i(\mathfrak{N} - \mathfrak{N}_1) = 0$$

and, by taking adjoints,

$$\mathfrak{M} - \mathfrak{M}_1 - i(\mathfrak{N} - \mathfrak{N}_1) = 0,$$

which implies that $\mathfrak{M} = \mathfrak{M}_1$, $\mathfrak{N} = \mathfrak{N}_1$. Furthermore,

$$\mathfrak{K}\mathfrak{K}^* = (\mathfrak{M} + i\mathfrak{N})(\mathfrak{M} - i\mathfrak{N}) = \mathfrak{M}^2 + \mathfrak{N}^2 + i(\mathfrak{N}\mathfrak{M} - \mathfrak{M}\mathfrak{N})$$

$$\mathfrak{K}^*\mathfrak{K} = (\mathfrak{M} - i\mathfrak{N})(\mathfrak{M} + i\mathfrak{N}) = \mathfrak{M}^2 + \mathfrak{N}^2 - i(\mathfrak{N}\mathfrak{M} - \mathfrak{M}\mathfrak{N}),$$

so that for a normal operator $\mathfrak{K}$ we must have $\mathfrak{M}\mathfrak{N} = \mathfrak{N}\mathfrak{M}$—a necessary and sufficient condition for $\mathfrak{K}$ to be normal. In other words, *an operator is normal if and only if its self-adjoint components commute.*

Let us now assume that $\mathfrak{K}$ is not only normal but also completely continuous. Let us suppose that we have chosen a complete orthonormal system made up of null solutions and eigenvectors of $\mathfrak{M}$. Then the associated kernel matrix is a diagonal matrix, having as diagonal entries either the inverse eigenvalues $\mu_\alpha = 1/\lambda_\alpha$ or else zeros. This matrix must commute with the kernel matrix of $\mathfrak{N}$, for the matrix associated with the product of two bounded operators is the product of the matrices associated with these operators, while the order of factors is the same for operators and associated matrices. Hence the elements $u_{\alpha\beta}$ of $\mathfrak{N}$ satisfy the relation

$$\mu_\alpha u_{\alpha\beta} = u_{\alpha\beta}\mu_\beta.$$

If $\mu_\alpha \neq \mu_\beta$ we must have $u_{\alpha\beta} = 0$. This tells us that if μ_α has multiplicity p, then to this group of p successive diagonal entries of $\mathfrak{M}$ there corresponds a $p \times p$ Hermitian diagonal block of $\mathfrak{N}$. The diagonal block of $\mathfrak{N}$ corresponding to the chain of zeros on the diagonal of $\mathfrak{M}$ is of finite or countably infinite order and is Hermitian and completely continuous. By choosing a basis of eigenvectors and null solutions of $\mathfrak{N}$ in the null space of $\mathfrak{M}$ and in the eigenmanifolds (that is, spaces of eigenvectors) associated with the reciprocal eigenvalues μ_α of $\mathfrak{M}$ we can diagonalize $\mathfrak{N}$ without affecting the diagonal form of $\mathfrak{M}$. The diagonal entries of $\mathfrak{N}$ would then be its reciprocal eigenvalues ν_α or zeros. If this is done, then the kernel matrix of

$\mathfrak{K} = \mathfrak{M} + i\mathfrak{N}$ is also in diagonal form and its diagonal entries are the reciprocal eigenvalues $\mu_\alpha + i\nu_\alpha$ of $\mathfrak{K}$ or zeros. Here μ_α or ν_α may be zero.

To sum up:

Every completely continuous normal operator distinct from the null operator possesses either a finite number of eigenvalues (degenerate case) or else an infinity of eigenvalues $1/(\mu_\alpha + i\nu_\alpha)$ (in general complex numbers) with no finite point of accumulation. Each eigenvalue has finite multiplicity. The union of the null vectors and eigenvectors of this operator contains a complete orthonormal system. The "expansion formula" and the "fundamental formula" still hold. The Hermitian components $\mathfrak{M}$ and $\mathfrak{N}$ of $\mathfrak{K}$ have the respective eigenvalues $1/\mu_\alpha$ and $1/\nu_\alpha$. If all the eigenvalues of $\mathfrak{K}$ are real, then $\mathfrak{N} = 0$ and $\mathfrak{K}$ is self-adjoint. In any case, $\mathfrak{K}$ and $\mathfrak{K}^*$ possess the same null vectors and eigenvectors. Conversely, if a completely continuous operator $\mathfrak{K}$ has the same null vectors and eigenvectors as $\mathfrak{K}^*$ and if the union of its null vectors and eigenvectors contains a complete orthonormal system, then $\mathfrak{K}$ must be normal.

We leave it to the reader to establish those of the above contentions which we have not already established above. This should present no difficulties.

§9. Positive Bounded Self-Adjoint Operators and Their Square Roots

1. The Existence and Uniqueness of the Square Root

In what follows we once again take up the study of bounded operators. Among bounded self-adjoint operators those of the form $\mathfrak{K}\mathfrak{K}^*$ are positive, i.e., for any y in $\mathfrak{H}$ we have $(\mathfrak{K}\mathfrak{K}^*y, y) = \|\mathfrak{K}^*y\|^2 \geqq 0$. In general, we shall say that a bounded self-adjoint operator $\mathfrak{K} = \mathfrak{K}^*$ is positive if $(\mathfrak{K}y, y) \geqq 0$ for all y in $\mathfrak{H}$. We wish to define an operator $\mathfrak{W} = \sqrt{\mathfrak{K}}$ in such a way that $\mathfrak{W}$, like $\mathfrak{K}$, is positive, self-adjoint, and satisfies the relation $\mathfrak{W}^2 = \mathfrak{K}$.

We can assume that $0 \leqq (\mathfrak{K}y, y) \leqq \|y\|^2$. This may require multiplication by a suitable positive factor. We now show that $\|\mathfrak{R}\| \leqq 1$. It is always true that 4·real part of $(\mathfrak{R}y, z) = (\mathfrak{R}(y+z), y+z) - (\mathfrak{R}(y-z), y-z) \leqq \|y+z\|^2 + \|y-z\|^2 = 2\{\|y\|^2 + \|z\|^2\}$. If in this relation we replace y by λy and z by $(1/\lambda)z$ (λ real), we obtain

$$4\cdot\text{real part of}\left(\mathfrak{R}\lambda y, \frac{1}{\lambda}z\right) = 4\cdot\text{real part of }(\mathfrak{R}y, z) \leqq 2\left\{\lambda^2\|y\|^2 + \frac{1}{\lambda^2}\|z\|^2\right\}.$$

The minimum value of the right side above is $4\|y\|\cdot\|z\|$. If we put $z = \mathfrak{R}y$, this implies that

$$(\mathfrak{R}y, \mathfrak{R}y) \leqq \|y\|\cdot\|\mathfrak{R}y\|,$$

$$\|\mathfrak{R}y\| \leqq \|y\|, \qquad \text{i.e.,} \qquad \|\mathfrak{R}\| \leqq 1.$$

We then have $(y, y) \geqq (y - \mathfrak{R}y, y) \geqq 0$, and therefore $\mathfrak{I} - \mathfrak{R} = \mathfrak{L}$ is likewise positive and self-adjoint and $\|\mathfrak{L}\| \leqq 1$. Formal expansion of $(\mathfrak{I} - \mathfrak{L})^{1/2}$ yields

$$\mathfrak{M} = \mathfrak{I} - \tfrac{1}{2}\mathfrak{L} + \frac{\frac{1}{2}(\frac{1}{2}-1)}{1\cdot 2}\mathfrak{L}^2 - \frac{\frac{1}{2}(\frac{1}{2}-1)(\frac{1}{2}-2)}{1\cdot 2\cdot 3}\mathfrak{L}^3 + \cdots.$$

Since the series

$$1 + \frac{1}{2}\cdot\|\mathfrak{L}\| + \frac{1}{2\cdot 4}\cdot\|\mathfrak{L}\|^2 + \frac{1\cdot 3}{2\cdot 4\cdot 6}\cdot\|\mathfrak{L}\|^3 + \cdots + \frac{1\cdot 3\cdots(2\nu-1)}{2\cdot 4\cdots(2\nu+2)}\|\mathfrak{L}\|^\nu + \cdots$$

converges for all possible values of $\|\mathfrak{L}\| \leqq 1$,[10] our operator

[10] This contention is clear for $\|\mathfrak{L}\| < 1$. If $\|\mathfrak{L}\| = 1$ it follows from Raabe's convergence test that $|a_{\nu+1}/a_\nu| \leqq 1 - \alpha/\nu$ ($\alpha > 1$)—for in the case at hand, this quotient $= (2\nu+1)/(2\nu+4) = 1 - 3/(2\nu+4) < 1 - 4/3\nu$ as soon as $\nu > 16$. We can demonstrate Raabe's criterion with the help of the convergent series $\sum_{n=1}^{\infty} 1/n^\alpha$ ($\alpha > 1$). We have $\sum_{n=2}^{N} 1/n^\alpha \leqq \int_{x=1}^{N} dx/x^\alpha \leqq 1/(\alpha - 1)$ while, by Bernoulli's inequality

$$\frac{1/n^\alpha}{1/(n-1)^\alpha} = \left(1 - \frac{1}{n}\right)^\alpha > 1 - \frac{\alpha}{n}.$$

series must likewise converge to a limit operator. This operator is bounded; in fact, its norm is bounded by the sum of the series in $\|\mathfrak{L}\|$. In addition, we see that $\mathfrak{W}^2 = \mathfrak{I} - \mathfrak{L} = \mathfrak{K}$; this is an immediate consequence of the structure of the above binomial series—we can operate with such power series of operators within their domain of convergence exactly as with ordinary power series. Furthermore, $\mathfrak{W}$ commutes with $\mathfrak{K}$ and even commutes with all self-adjoint bounded operators which commute with $\mathfrak{K}$. We shall henceforth denote such a type of cummutativity by the symbol $\mathfrak{W}\ \mathrm{cc}\ \mathfrak{K}$. Lastly, $\mathfrak{W}$ must be Hermitian and positive, for we have

$$(\mathfrak{W}y, y) \geqq \|y\|^2 \cdot \left(1 - \tfrac{1}{2}\|\mathfrak{L}\| - \cdots - \frac{1\cdot 3\cdots(2\nu-1)}{2\cdot 4\cdots(2\nu+2)}\cdot\|\mathfrak{L}\|^\nu - \cdots\right),$$

where the quantity in parentheses is convergent and $\geqq 0$ (for it equals $\sqrt{1-\|\mathfrak{L}\|}$ which is $\geqq 0$). From $\mathfrak{W}^2 = \mathfrak{K}$ we see that $\|\mathfrak{W}\| = \sqrt{\|\mathfrak{K}\|}$, since $(\mathfrak{W}y, \mathfrak{W}y) = (\mathfrak{K}y, y) \leqq \|\mathfrak{K}\|\cdot\|y\|^2$; hence $\|\mathfrak{W}y\| \leqq \sqrt{\|\mathfrak{K}\|}\cdot\|y\|$ and no bound exists which is $< \sqrt{\|\mathfrak{K}\|}$.

The above positive square root of $\mathfrak{K}$ *is unique.* For if $\mathfrak{B}$ were another positive bounded self-adjoint square root of $\mathfrak{K}$, we would have $\mathfrak{B}^2 = \mathfrak{K}$ and $\mathfrak{B}\mathfrak{K} = \mathfrak{K}\mathfrak{B} = \mathfrak{B}^3$. Hence $\mathfrak{B}$ would commute with $\mathfrak{K}$ and therefore also with $\mathfrak{W}$. Now let $\sqrt{\mathfrak{B}}$ and $\sqrt{\mathfrak{W}}$ denote positive square roots of $\mathfrak{B}$ and $\mathfrak{W}$ (such square roots exist). For any y in $\mathfrak{H}$ let $x = (\mathfrak{W} - \mathfrak{B})y$. Then $\|\sqrt{\mathfrak{W}}x\|^2 + \|\sqrt{\mathfrak{B}}x\|^2 = (\mathfrak{W}x, x) + (\mathfrak{B}x, x) = ((\mathfrak{W}+\mathfrak{B})(\mathfrak{W}-\mathfrak{B})y, x) = ((\mathfrak{W}^2 - \mathfrak{B}^2)y, x) = 0$, hence $\sqrt{\mathfrak{W}}x = 0$, $\sqrt{\mathfrak{B}}x = 0$, $\mathfrak{W}x = 0$, $\mathfrak{B}x = 0$, and, furthermore,

$$\|(\mathfrak{W} - \mathfrak{B})y\|^2 = ((\mathfrak{W} - \mathfrak{B})^2 y, y) = ((\mathfrak{W} - \mathfrak{B})x, y) = 0, \qquad \text{i.e.,}$$

$$(\mathfrak{W} - \mathfrak{B})y = 0 \qquad \mathfrak{W}y = \mathfrak{B}y \qquad \mathfrak{W} = \mathfrak{B}.$$

2. *The Toeplitz Theorems on Inverse Operators*

In the special case where, for all $y \neq 0$, we have $(\mathfrak{K}y, y) > 0$, we shall say that $\mathfrak{K}$ is positive definite.

Suppose the bounded operator $\mathfrak{K}y = x$ *has an inverse* $\mathfrak{K}^{-1}$,

$\mathfrak{R}\mathfrak{R}^{-1} = \mathfrak{R}^{-1}\mathfrak{R} = \mathfrak{I}$, which is bounded and thus defined for all x. Then $\mathfrak{R}\mathfrak{R}^*$ and $\mathfrak{R}^*\mathfrak{R}$ must be positive definite; more specifically, we must have

$$m\|y\|^2 \leqq (\mathfrak{R}^*\mathfrak{R}y, y) \leqq M\|y\|^2 \qquad (m > 0; \quad M = \|\mathfrak{R}\|^2 > 0)$$
$$m\|y\|^2 \leqq (\mathfrak{R}\mathfrak{R}^*y, y) \leqq M\|y\|^2.$$

For if we put $\mathfrak{R}^*\mathfrak{R} = \mathfrak{L} = \mathfrak{L}^*$, then, clearly, the right side of the first of these inequalities holds. To prove the left side of this inequality, note that if

$$\mathfrak{R}y = x, \quad y = \mathfrak{R}^{-1}x, \qquad \text{then} \qquad \mathfrak{R}^{-1}(\mathfrak{R}y) = y,$$

so that $(y, y) = (\mathfrak{R}^{-1}\mathfrak{R}y, y) \leqq \|\mathfrak{R}^{-1}\| \cdot \|\mathfrak{R}y\| \cdot \|y\|$, $\|\mathfrak{R}y\| \geqq 1/\|\mathfrak{R}^{-1}\| \cdot \|y\|$. If we put $m = 1/\|\mathfrak{R}^{-1}\|^2$, our contention follows. Similar arguments will prove the other inequalities.

Conversely, if for a bounded operator $\mathfrak{R}$ we have

$$m\|y\|^2 \leqq (\mathfrak{R}^*\mathfrak{R}y, y) \leqq M\|y\|^2$$
$$m\|y\|^2 \leqq (\mathfrak{R}\mathfrak{R}^*y, y) \leqq M\|y\|^2$$

for all y in $\mathfrak{H}$, then $\mathfrak{R}$ possesses a bounded inverse, i.e., $\mathfrak{R}^{-1}\mathfrak{R} = \mathfrak{R}\mathfrak{R}^{-1} = \mathfrak{I}$.

We first show that this is true for $\mathfrak{L} = \mathfrak{R}^*\mathfrak{R}$. Then for an appropriately chosen positive factor σ such that $\sigma m < \sigma M < 1$ we have $(\sigma\mathfrak{L}y, y) < \|y\|^2$, whence $0 < ((\mathfrak{I} - \sigma\mathfrak{L})y, y) \leqq (1 - \sigma m) \cdot \|y\|^2 < \|y\|^2$. Therefore $\|\sqrt{\mathfrak{I} - \sigma\mathfrak{L}}\| < 1$, $\|\mathfrak{I} - \sigma\mathfrak{L}\| < 1$, and the series

$$\mathfrak{I} + (\mathfrak{I} - \sigma\mathfrak{L}) + (\mathfrak{I} - \sigma\mathfrak{L})^2 + \cdots$$

must converge. The sum of this series of operators is the inverse of $\mathfrak{I} - (\mathfrak{I} - \sigma\mathfrak{L}) = \sigma\mathfrak{L}$ and its norm has the upper bound $1/(1 - (1 - \sigma m)) = 1/\sigma m$. Hence $\mathfrak{L}^{-1}$ exists for all x and is positive definite, Hermitian, and bounded in norm by $1/m$. From $\mathfrak{R}y = x$ it follows, therefore, that $\mathfrak{L}^{-1}\mathfrak{R}^*\mathfrak{R}y = y = \mathfrak{L}^{-1}\mathfrak{R}^*x$; hence $\mathfrak{N} = \mathfrak{L}^{-1}\mathfrak{R}^*$ is defined for all x in $\mathfrak{H}$ and bounded. We have $\mathfrak{N}\mathfrak{R} = \mathfrak{I}$ and if we also have $m\|y\|^2 \leqq (\mathfrak{R}\mathfrak{R}^*y, y) \leqq M\|y\|^2$ with $m > 0$, then we can deduce, as above, the existence of a bounded operator $\mathfrak{N}_1$ with $\mathfrak{N}_1\mathfrak{R}^* = \mathfrak{I}$. But then $\mathfrak{K}\mathfrak{R}_1{}^* = \mathfrak{I}$, $\mathfrak{R}_1{}^* = \mathfrak{R}\mathfrak{K}\mathfrak{R}_1{}^* = \mathfrak{R}$, and, finally, $\mathfrak{K}\mathfrak{R} = \mathfrak{I}$. *In this case the bounded inverse* $\mathfrak{K}^{-1}$ *just obtained must be unique.* Indeed, suppose $\mathfrak{R}$ were a second operator satisfying $\mathfrak{R}\mathfrak{K} = \mathfrak{K}\mathfrak{R} = \mathfrak{I}$. Then $\mathfrak{K}\cdot(\mathfrak{R} - \mathfrak{K}^{-1})y = 0$ for all y. If we put $z = (\mathfrak{R} - \mathfrak{K}^{-1})y$, then $\mathfrak{K}z = 0$ and, since $(\mathfrak{K}^*\mathfrak{K}z, z) \geqq m\|z\|^2$, we must have $z = 0$, i.e., $\mathfrak{R}y = \mathfrak{K}^{-1}y$.[11]

If $\mathfrak{K}$ is bounded but the largest possible m in the first double inequality on p. 63 is zero, then we still have $0 \leqq (\mathfrak{K}^*\mathfrak{K}y, y) \leqq M\|y\|^2$. There must then exist a sequence y_n where $\|y_n\| = 1$, such that

$$(\mathfrak{K}^*\mathfrak{K}y_n, y_n) \to 0, \qquad \text{i.e.,} \qquad \|\mathfrak{K}y_n\| \to 0, \quad \mathfrak{K}y_n \to 0.$$

This precludes the existence of a bounded left inverse $\mathfrak{R}$, for if $\mathfrak{R}\mathfrak{K} = \mathfrak{I}$, then $\mathfrak{R}\mathfrak{K}y_n = y_n$ whence $\|y_n\| \to 0$, and this contradicts the fact that $\|y_n\| = 1$. If, at the same time, the double inequality

$$m\|y\|^2 \leqq (\mathfrak{K}\mathfrak{K}^*y, y) \leqq M\|y\|^2$$

(cf. p. 63)
holds with $m > 0$, then, as above, we can deduce the existence of a left inverse $\mathfrak{R}^*$ of $\mathfrak{K}^*$ i.e., a right inverse of $\mathfrak{K}$, $\mathfrak{K}\mathfrak{R} = \mathfrak{I}$. All in all, the following results are valid:

The bounded but otherwise arbitrary operator $\mathfrak{K}$ *possesses*

(1) *either a uniquely determined, bounded, simultaneously left and right inverse* $\mathfrak{K}^{-1}$,

(2) *or a left, but not a right, bounded inverse,*

(3) *or a right, but not a left, bounded inverse,*

(4) *or neither a left nor a right bounded inverse.*

If a left (or right) bounded inverse exists and is unique, then we must of necessity be in case 1. In cases 2 and 3 there exists an infinity of left (or right) inverses.

The last two contentions can be proved as follows: From $\mathfrak{R}\mathfrak{K} = \mathfrak{I}$ it follows that $\mathfrak{K}\mathfrak{R}\mathfrak{K} = \mathfrak{K}$ and so $(\mathfrak{K}\mathfrak{R} - \mathfrak{I})\mathfrak{K} = 0$. If $\mathfrak{K}\mathfrak{R} - \mathfrak{I} = \mathfrak{L} \neq 0$, then, besides $\mathfrak{R}$, the operators $\mathfrak{R} + c\mathfrak{L}$ are also left inverses of $\mathfrak{K}$, for $(\mathfrak{R} + c\mathfrak{L})\mathfrak{K} = \mathfrak{I}$.

[11] Proof that $\mathfrak{R} = \mathfrak{K}^{-1}$: $\mathfrak{R} = (\mathfrak{K}^{-1}\mathfrak{K})\mathfrak{R} = \mathfrak{K}^{-1}(\mathfrak{K}\mathfrak{R}) = \mathfrak{K}^{-1}$. (Ed.)

3. Normalizable Operators

Throughout this section $\mathfrak{D}$ will denote a positive definite Hermitian operator for which we assume that

$$m\|y\|^2 \leqq (\mathfrak{D}y, y) \leqq M\|y\|^2, \qquad m > 0.$$

This assumption is equivalent to the existence of $\mathfrak{D}^{-1}$.

Using $\mathfrak{D}$ we can introduce in $\mathfrak{H}$ a new scalar product[12] defined by $[x, y] = (x, \mathfrak{D}y) = (\mathfrak{D}x, y)$. Then the "square of the norm" becomes $[x]^2 = [x, x] = (x, \mathfrak{D}x)$. If $[x] = 0$, then $x = 0$ and all the axioms (a), (b), (c), (d) of §2 hold. In other words, we have defined a new Hilbert space $[\mathfrak{H}]$ having the same elements as $\mathfrak{H}$. Of course, the definitions of strong and weak convergence must be reformulated; however, it turns out that (strong and weak) convergence in $\mathfrak{H}$ is equivalent to convergence in $[\mathfrak{H}]$.

A normal completely continuous operator $\mathfrak{K}$ in $[\mathfrak{H}]$ is characterized by $\mathfrak{K}^{[*]}\mathfrak{K} = \mathfrak{K}\mathfrak{K}^{[*]}$, where $\mathfrak{K}^{[*]}$ is defined by

$$[\mathfrak{K}y, x] = [y, \mathfrak{K}^{[*]}x].$$

One can easily show that $\mathfrak{K}^{[*]} = \mathfrak{D}^{-1}\mathfrak{K}^*\mathfrak{D}$ in $\mathfrak{H}$, in particular, $\mathfrak{D}^{[*]} = \mathfrak{D}$. The theorem of §8 on completely continuous normal operators is fully applicable to $\mathfrak{K}$; in particular, we may assert the existence of an associated complete orthonormal system composed of null vectors and eigenvectors. Such an orthonormal system contains elements y_α for which

$$[y_\alpha, y_\beta] = (y_\alpha, \mathfrak{D}y_\beta) = \delta_{\alpha\beta}.$$

In $\mathfrak{H}$, $\mathfrak{K}$ satisfies the relation $\mathfrak{K}\mathfrak{D}^{-1}\mathfrak{K}^*\mathfrak{D} = \mathfrak{D}^{-1}\mathfrak{K}^*\mathfrak{D}\mathfrak{K}$. If we put $\mathfrak{K} = \mathfrak{L}\mathfrak{D}$, $\mathfrak{K}^* = \mathfrak{D}\mathfrak{L}^*$, then $\mathfrak{L}\mathfrak{D}\mathfrak{L}^* = \mathfrak{L}^*\mathfrak{D}\mathfrak{L}$, a generalization of the defining condition for normal operators; we shall call $\mathfrak{K}$ normalizable in $\mathfrak{H}$. If we put $\mathfrak{P} = \sqrt{\mathfrak{D}^{-1}}$, then $\mathfrak{P}^{-1}\mathfrak{K}\mathfrak{P} = \sqrt{\mathfrak{D}}\mathfrak{L}\mathfrak{D}\sqrt{\mathfrak{D}^{-1}} = \sqrt{\mathfrak{D}}\mathfrak{L}\sqrt{\mathfrak{D}} = \mathfrak{N}$, and this operator is normal in $\mathfrak{H}$. In fact,

$$\begin{aligned}\mathfrak{N}\mathfrak{N}^* = \sqrt{\mathfrak{D}}\mathfrak{L}\sqrt{\mathfrak{D}}\sqrt{\mathfrak{D}}\cdot\mathfrak{L}^*\sqrt{\mathfrak{D}} &= \sqrt{\mathfrak{D}}\mathfrak{L}\mathfrak{D}\mathfrak{L}^*\sqrt{\mathfrak{D}} \\ &= \sqrt{\mathfrak{D}}\mathfrak{L}^*\mathfrak{D}\mathfrak{L}\sqrt{\mathfrak{D}} = \mathfrak{N}^*\mathfrak{N}.\end{aligned}$$

[12] This inner product determines a "non-Euclidean" distance in $\mathfrak{H}$.

Hence our operator $\mathfrak{K}$ is "similar" to a normal operator. Conversely, suppose $\mathfrak{K}$ is any operator similar to a normal operator, i.e., $\mathfrak{P}^{-1}\mathfrak{K}\mathfrak{P} = \mathfrak{N}$, where $\mathfrak{P}$ and $\mathfrak{P}^{-1}$ are bounded. If we put $\mathfrak{D} = \mathfrak{P}^{*-1}\mathfrak{P}^{-1}$, then $\mathfrak{D}$ possesses the properties listed above and we have

$$\mathfrak{K}\mathfrak{D}^{-1}\mathfrak{K}^*\mathfrak{D} = \mathfrak{P}\mathfrak{N}\mathfrak{P}^{-1}\cdot\mathfrak{P}\mathfrak{P}^*\cdot\mathfrak{P}^{*-1}\mathfrak{N}^*\mathfrak{P}^*\mathfrak{P}^{*-1}\mathfrak{P}^{-1}$$

$$= \mathfrak{P}\mathfrak{N}\mathfrak{N}^*\mathfrak{P}^{-1},$$

$$\mathfrak{D}^{-1}\mathfrak{K}^*\mathfrak{D}\mathfrak{K} = \mathfrak{P}\mathfrak{P}^*\cdot\mathfrak{P}^{*-1}\mathfrak{N}^*\mathfrak{P}^*\cdot\mathfrak{P}^{*-1}\mathfrak{P}^{-1}\cdot\mathfrak{P}\mathfrak{N}\mathfrak{P}^{-1}$$

$$= \mathfrak{P}\mathfrak{N}^*\mathfrak{N}\mathfrak{P}^{-1},$$

i.e., both these lines are identical and therefore $\mathfrak{K}\mathfrak{K}^{[*]} = \mathfrak{K}^{[*]}\mathfrak{K}$ in $[\mathfrak{H}]$. Thus, *every normal operator* $\mathfrak{K}$ *in* $[\mathfrak{H}]$ *is similar to a normal operator in* $\mathfrak{H}$ (i.e., normalizable), *and conversely.* Note that in the notation $\mathfrak{K} = \mathfrak{L}\mathfrak{D}$ the right factor seems to have been singled out; however, we could also have written $\mathfrak{K} = \mathfrak{D}^{-1}\mathfrak{L}_1$, where $\mathfrak{L}_1 = \mathfrak{D}\mathfrak{L}\mathfrak{D}$, and we would have found that $\mathfrak{D}^{-1}$ and $\mathfrak{L}_1$ satisfied the relation $\mathfrak{L}_1\mathfrak{D}^{-1}\mathfrak{L}_1{}^* = \mathfrak{L}_1{}^*\mathfrak{D}^{-1}\mathfrak{L}_1$ similar to that previously found for $\mathfrak{D}$ and $\mathfrak{L}$.

The complete orthonormal system y_α in $[\mathfrak{H}]$ viewed in $\mathfrak{H}$ becomes a complete bounded biorthogonal system $y_1, y_2, \cdots$; $\mathfrak{D}y_1, \mathfrak{D}y_2, \cdots$, for, putting $y_\alpha = \mathfrak{P}\varphi_\alpha = u_\alpha$, then $\mathfrak{D}y_\alpha = \mathfrak{P}^{*-1}\varphi_\alpha = v_\alpha$ and $(\varphi_\alpha, \varphi_\beta) = (\mathfrak{P}^{-1}y_\alpha, \mathfrak{P}^{-1}y_\beta) = (y_\alpha, \mathfrak{P}^{*-1}\mathfrak{P}^{-1}y_\beta) = (y_\alpha, \mathfrak{D}y_\beta) = \delta_{\alpha\beta}$, and therefore the φ_α form a complete[13] orthonormal system in $\mathfrak{H}$, while, by §5, the biorthogonal system is complete and bounded. We leave it to the reader to establish the following result:

A completely continuous operator $\mathfrak{K}$ *in* $\mathfrak{H}$ *can be normalized if and only if the null vectors and eigenvectors of* $\mathfrak{K}$ *and* $\mathfrak{K}^*$ *taken together contain a complete bounded biorthogonal system.*

[13] The y_α form a fundamental system in $[\mathfrak{H}]$ and therefore in $\mathfrak{H}$ (since convergence is preserved). Hence the $\varphi_\alpha = \mathfrak{P}^{-1}y_\alpha$ also form a fundamental system in $\mathfrak{H}$. An orthonormal system which is also a fundamental system is a complete orthonormal system. (Ed.)

§10. More on Completely Continuous Operators

1. The Normal Component Associated with an Eigenvalue

We have shown that a normalizable completely continuous operator always has eigenvalues. Our proof is not valid for *arbitrary* completely continuous operators, for there exist examples of such operators having no eigenvalues (e.g., $\mathfrak{K}y = \int_a^s K(s, t)y(t)\,dt$ with a continuous kernel in $\mathfrak{L}^2(a, b)$ has no eigenvalues).

In what follows *we shall always assume that the completely continuous operator we are dealing with has at least one eigenvalue*, and then examine how, by means of similarity transformations, we can represent our operator in as simple a way as possible. We have already been introduced to such transformations in our study of normalizable operators; they are a generalization of orthogonal transformations which play an analogous role in the representation of self-adjoint and normal operators. This, in slightly different language, means that we shall seek to represent the operator $\mathfrak{K}$ by means of a suitable biorthogonal system rather than by means of an orthogonal system, as we did previously. Insofar as this biorthogonal system is associated with the eigenvalue we have assumed to exist it will be an incomplete system, just as in the case of a normal operator where each eigenvalue leads to the incomplete orthonormal system of associated eigenvectors.

Let $\mathfrak{K}$, then, be a completely continuous operator which maps $\mathfrak{H}$ into itself, and let $\lambda \neq 0$ be an eigenvalue of $\mathfrak{K}$. Then there exists a solution to the equation

$$\mu y = \mathfrak{K}y \qquad (\|y\| \neq 0) \quad (\mu = 1/\lambda).$$

By the Fredholm theorems there also exists a solution to

$$\bar{\mu}x = \mathfrak{K}^*x \qquad (\|x\| \neq 0).$$

The number of linearly independent solutions is finite and the same for both equations. There arise two mutually exclusive possibilities:

I. All solutions x are orthogonal to all solutions y.

II. For at least one y we can find an x such that $(y, x) = 1$.

First we examine case II, putting $y = y_1$, $x = x_1$, and $(y_1, x_1) = 1$. By the method of §5 we now extend this incomplete bounded biorthogonal system to a complete bounded biorthogonal system $y_1, y_2, \cdots ; x_1, x_2, \cdots$. Then every element y can be written in the form $y = (y, x_1)y_1 + y'$, where $(y', x_1) = 0$. Thus we have

$$\mathfrak{K}y = (y, x_1)\mathfrak{K}y_1 + \mathfrak{K}y' = \mu(y, x_1)y_1 + \mathfrak{K}y',$$

and $(\mathfrak{K}y', x_1) = (y', \mathfrak{K}^*x_1) = \mu(y', x_1) = 0$. The subspace of all y' such that $(y', x_1) = 0$ is generated by $y_2, y_3, \cdots$ and is mapped by the operator $\mathfrak{K}$ into itself; we have, so to speak, a splitting-off of a one-element part $\mu(y, x)y_1$ of $\mathfrak{K}y$, enabling us to study $\mathfrak{K}$ over the subspace $(y_2, y_3, \cdots)$. Similarly, every x can be written in the form $x = (x, y_1)x_1 + x'$, $(y_1, x') = 0$, and $\mathfrak{K}^*x = (x, y_1)\cdot \mathfrak{K}^*x_1 + \mathfrak{K}^*x' = \bar{\mu}(x, y_1)x_1 + \mathfrak{K}^*x'$. Furthermore, $(y_1, \mathfrak{K}^*x') = (\mathfrak{K}y_1, x') = \mu(y_1, x') = 0$, so that $\mathfrak{K}^*x'$ also lies in the same subspace as x'. If on repeating our procedure within the subspace we still find ourselves in case II, we can again detach a one-element part from the vectors $\mathfrak{K}y$ and $\mathfrak{K}^*x$ and repeat our procedure as long as there are eigenvalues leading to case II.

We now examine case I. Let us again assume that y_1 is a solution of the equation $\mu y = \mathfrak{K}y$, and x_1 is a solution of the equation $\bar{\mu}x = \mathfrak{K}^*x$. Since y_1 is orthogonal to all such x_1, Fredholm's third theorem implies that the equation

$$\mathfrak{K}y_2 = y_1 + \mu y_2$$

has a solution y_2. If $(y_2, x_1) = 0$ for all x_1, then the equation

$$\mathfrak{K}y_3 = y_2 + \mu y_3$$

has a solution y_3, again according to Fredholm's third theorem. We can repeat this procedure as long as the solution to an equation is orthogonal to all x_1. Suppose $y_1, y_2, \cdots, y_k$ is a chain of elements which have been generated from y_1 by the above procedure, i.e., $\mathfrak{K}y_\alpha = y_{\alpha-1} + \mu y_\alpha$. Then $(y_1, x_1) = \cdots = (y_{k-1}, x_1) = 0$ for each x_1 satisfying the equation $\mathfrak{K}^*x_1 = \bar{\mu}x_1$.

We contend that $y_1, \cdots, y_k$ must be linearly independent. Indeed, suppose

$$c_1 y_1 + c_2 y_2 + \cdots + c_k y_k = 0 \qquad (c_l \neq 0, \quad l \leq k),$$

where the number l of elements in this relation is chosen to be minimal. If we apply the operator $\mathfrak{K} - \mu\mathfrak{J}$ to this equation, we obtain

$$c_2 y_1 + \cdots + c_l y_{l-1} = 0,$$

contradicting the above minimality assumption.

Let us now orthogonalize the chain $y_1, \cdots, y_k$ and let $y_1^*, \cdots, y_k^*$ be the resulting orthonormal chain. Then y_α^* is a linear combination of $y_1, \cdots, y_\alpha$ while y_α is, in turn, a linear combination of $y_1^*, \cdots, y_\alpha^*$. It follows that $\mathfrak{K}y_\alpha$ can be represented as a combination of $y_1^*, \cdots, y_\alpha^*$, and $(\mathfrak{K}y_\alpha - \mu y_\alpha, y_\alpha^*) = 0$. This implies that $(\mathfrak{K}y_\alpha^* - \mu y_\alpha^*, y_\alpha^*) = 0$, i.e.,

$$\frac{1}{\mu}(\mathfrak{K}y_\alpha^*, y_\alpha^*) = 1.$$

If the above chain could be made infinitely long, then, since $y_\alpha^* \rightharpoonup 0$ and $\mathfrak{K}$ is completely continuous, we would also have $(\mathfrak{K}y_\alpha^*, y_\alpha^*) \to 0$, which is a contradiction. To sum up:

With every element y_1 which satisfies the equation $\mu y_1 = \mathfrak{K}y_1$ we can associate a finite chain of derived elements $y_2, \cdots, y_k$ satisfying $(y_1, x_1) = \cdots = (y_{k-1}, x_1) = 0$ while for the last element y_k we can find an x_1 such that $(y_k, x_1) = 1$. That $(y_k, x_1) = 1$ follows from the fact that our chain could otherwise be continued at least one more step.

We may now start from x_1 and proceed in a way "dual" to our previous procedure, studying

$$\mathfrak{K}^* x_2 = x_1 + \bar{\mu} x_2.$$

This equation has a solution, since x_1 is orthogonal to all the solutions y_1 of the equation $\mathfrak{K}y_1 = \mu y_1$. The scalar product (y_α, x_1) equals $(y_\alpha, \mathfrak{K}^* x_2 - \bar{\mu} x_2) = (\mathfrak{K}y_\alpha - \mu y_\alpha, x_2) = (y_{\alpha-1}, x_2)$ $(\alpha = 2, \cdots, k)$, so that $(y_1, x_2) = 0, \cdots, (y_{k-2}, x_2) = 0$, $(y_{k-1}, x_2) = (y_k, x_1) = 1$. We may assume that $(y_k, x_2) = 0$; for if this is not the case we can choose in place of y_k an appropriate element of the form $y_k + cy_{k-1}$.[14]

For $k = 2$ we see that the elements

$$\begin{matrix} y_1 & y_2 \\ x_2 & x_1 \end{matrix}$$

form a biorthogonal system such that the scalar products (y_α, x_β) equal one if α and β occur in the same column of the above table and otherwise $(y_\alpha, x_\beta) = 0$.

Now let $k > 2$, and let us further suppose that if y_1 satisfies $\mu y_1 = \mathfrak{K} y_1$, then it cannot generate a chain of length exactly 2. Consider the equation

$$\mathfrak{K}^* x_3 = x_2 + \bar{\mu} x_3.$$

This equation has a solution, for (x_2, y_1) is always zero. Indeed, if there existed a y_1 such that $(x_2, y_1) \neq 0$, then the chain derivable from this y_1 would be of length two, for we would have $(y_2, x_1) = (y_1, x_2) \neq 0$, and hence our procedure could not be continued.

Now suppose $k = 3$. Then $(y_1, x_3) = (y_3, x_1) = 1, (y_2, x_3) = 0$ and if we appropriately choose $y_3(+cy_1)$, then also $(y_3, x_3) = 0$. Then

$$\begin{matrix} y_1 & y_2 & y_3 \\ x_3 & x_2 & x_1 \end{matrix}$$

forms a biorthogonal system where elements in the same column have a scalar product of one, while all other products $(y_\alpha, x_\beta) = 0$.

It should by now be clear how to continue the process. In general, among all y_1 we seek out a y_1 generating a chain of smallest possible length k and show, in exactly the same way as above, that the chain derivable from x_1 also has length k. Furthermore, the system

$$\begin{matrix} y_1 & y_2 & \cdots & y_k \\ x_k & x_{k-1} & \cdots & x_1 \end{matrix}$$

[14] This is justified by observing that the chain $y_1, y_2, \cdots, y_k$ can be replaced by the chain $y_1, y_2 + cy_1, \cdots, y_k + cy_{k-1}$. (Ed.)

is a biorthogonal system where elements in the same column have a scalar product of one, while all other products (y_α, x_β) are zero. By §5, we know that we can extend the above system to a complete bounded biorthogonal system $y_1, \cdots, y_k, y_{k+1}, \cdots$; $x_1, \cdots, x_k, x_{k+1}, \cdots$. We then have

$$\begin{aligned} \mathfrak{K} y_\alpha &= y_{\alpha-1} + \mu y_\alpha \\ \mathfrak{K}^* x_\alpha &= x_{\alpha-1} + \bar{\mu} x_\alpha \end{aligned} \qquad \begin{pmatrix} \alpha = 1, \cdots, k \\ x_0 = 0,\ y_0 = 0 \end{pmatrix}.$$

If we put

$$y = \sum_{\alpha=1}^{k} (y, x_{k-\alpha+1}) y_\alpha + y'$$

$$x = \sum_{\alpha=1}^{k} (x, y_{k-\alpha+1}) x_\alpha + x',$$

then $(x', y_\alpha) = 0$ $(\alpha = 1, \cdots, k)$, because x' is a combination of $x_{k+1}, \cdots$. Likewise, $(y', x_\alpha) = 0$. Furthermore,

$$\begin{aligned} \mathfrak{K} y &= \sum_{\alpha=1}^{k} (y, x_{k-\alpha+1}) \mathfrak{K} y_\alpha + \mathfrak{K} y' \\ &= \sum_{\alpha=1}^{k} (y, x_{k-\alpha+1})(y_{\alpha-1} + \mu y_\alpha) + \mathfrak{K} y' \end{aligned}$$

and $(\mathfrak{K} y', x_\alpha) = (y', \mathfrak{K}^* x_\alpha) = (y', x_{\alpha-1} + \bar{\mu} x_\alpha) = 0$, which tells us that $\mathfrak{K} y'$ belongs to the subspace $\mathfrak{H}_1$ generated by $y_{k+1}, \cdots$. In similar fashion, we find that $(\mathfrak{K}^* x', y_\alpha) = (x', \mathfrak{K} y_\alpha) = (x', y_{\alpha-1} + \mu y_\alpha) = 0$. Hence $\mathfrak{K} y'$ belongs to the same subspace as y' and $\mathfrak{K}^* x'$ belongs to the same subspace as x'. If another eigenvalue exists, we can repeat for it all the above considerations, etc.

In order to make these results appear more intuitive, we shall use the concept of the kernel matrix of an operator relative to a complete and bounded biorthogonal system rather than a complete orthonormal system with which we are familiar from §5.

Let us start from a given bounded (not necessarily completely continuous) operator $\mathfrak{K}$ with $\mathfrak{H}' = \mathfrak{H}$. Let $u_1, u_2, \cdots, v_1, v_2, \cdots$

be a complete bounded biorthogonal system in $\mathfrak{H}$. For any y in $\mathfrak{H}$ we have

$$\mathfrak{K}y = \sum_{\alpha=1}^{\infty} (\mathfrak{K}y, u_\alpha) v_\alpha.$$

If $\mathfrak{K}y = x$, then we must have

$$(\mathfrak{K}y, u_\alpha) = (y, \mathfrak{K}^* u_\alpha) = (x, u_\alpha) = a_\alpha$$

but, on the other hand, by the completeness condition, we have

$$(y, \mathfrak{K}^* u_\alpha) = \sum_{\beta=1}^{\infty} (y, u_\beta)(v_\beta, \mathfrak{K}^* u_\alpha).$$

If we put $(y, u_\beta) = y_\beta$ and

$$a_{\alpha\beta} = (v_\beta, \mathfrak{K}^* u_\alpha) = (\mathfrak{K} v_\beta, u_\alpha),$$

then

$$\sum_{\beta=1}^{\infty} a_{\alpha\beta} y_\beta = a_\alpha \qquad (\alpha = 1, 2, \cdots).$$

Hence, if $\mathfrak{K}y = x$ possesses a solution y in $\mathfrak{H}$, then the Fourier coefficients $y_\beta = (y, u_\beta)$ satisfy the above system of equations. Conversely, if this system has a square summable solution $(y_1, y_2, \cdots)$, then $y = \sum_{\beta=1}^{\infty} y_\beta v_\beta$ is in $\mathfrak{H}$ and

$$a_\alpha = \sum_{\beta=1}^{\infty} (v_\beta, \mathfrak{K}^* u_\alpha)(y, u_\beta) = (y, \mathfrak{K}^* u_\alpha) = (\mathfrak{K}y, u_\alpha) = (x, u_\alpha),$$

whence $\mathfrak{K}y = x$. Our operator equation is therefore equivalent to this system of equations. The matrix

$$(\mathfrak{K} v_\beta, u_\alpha) = a_{\alpha\beta}$$

is called the *kernel matrix of the operator with respect to the given complete and bounded biorthonormal system.*

If we identify $y_1, \cdots, y_k$ with $v_1, \cdots, v_k$ and $x_k, \cdots, x_1$ with $u_1, \cdots, u_k$, then the kernel matrix takes the form

$$(\mathfrak{K} v_\beta, u_\beta) = \begin{pmatrix} \mu & 1 & 0 & \cdots & 0 & \\ 0 & \mu & 1 & \cdots & 0 & \\ \cdots & \cdots & \cdots & \cdots & \cdots & 0 \\ 0 & 0 & 0 & \cdots & \mu & \\ & & 0 & & & \mathfrak{A}_1 \end{pmatrix}$$

Here $\mathfrak{A}_1$ denotes the kernel matrix of the appropriate restriction of $\mathfrak{K}$. In the case where $k = 1$, the first component simply stands for the diagonal entry μ. The kernel matrix is completely reduced. If another eigenvalue exists, the complete reduction can be continued, and so forth. Of course, each eigenvalue can occur only a finite number of times, because the number of solutions of the homogeneous equation $\mathfrak{K}y - \mu y = 0$ must be finite.

Now we can choose the different solutions of the homogeneous equation for a fixed μ to be orthogonal to each other, and, starting from each solution we can form a chain of derived elements. The totality of derived elements will be linearly independent. If $y_\alpha^{(\varrho)}$ denotes an element of the ϱth chain, then

$$\mathfrak{K}y_\alpha^{(\varrho)} = y_{\alpha-1}^{(\varrho)} + \mu y_\alpha^{(\varrho)} \qquad \begin{array}{l}(\varrho = 1, \cdots, r),\\ (\alpha = 1, \cdots, k_\varrho),\\ (k_1 + \cdots + k_r = m).\end{array}$$

Let us keep $y_1^{(1)}, \cdots, y_1^{(r)}$ fixed and orthogonalize the above elements forming a new set of elements $y_\alpha^{(\varrho)*}$. Then

$$\mathfrak{K}y_\alpha^{(\varrho)*} = \mu y_\alpha^{(\varrho)*} + (\cdots),$$

where the parentheses denote a linear combination of the other $y_\beta^{(\varrho)*}$. Clearly,

$$\|\mathfrak{K}y_\alpha^{(\varrho)*}\|^2 = (\mathfrak{K}y_\alpha^{(\varrho)*}, \mathfrak{K}y_\alpha^{(\varrho)*}) \geqq |\mu|^2.$$

Summing over α and ϱ we get the inequality

$$m|\mu|^2 \leqq \sum_{\substack{\alpha = 1, \cdots, k\varrho \\ \varrho = 1, \cdots, r}} \|\mathfrak{K}y_\alpha^{(\varrho)*}\|^2.$$

Now suppose that our operator has the property that for each complete orthonormal system $t_1, t_2, \cdots$ the series $\sum \|\mathfrak{K}t_\alpha\|^2$ converges (this condition holds, for example, for integral operators for which $\int_a^b \int_a^b |K(s, t)|^2 \, ds \, dt$ exists (cf. §6)). Let m_σ denote the "total multiplicity" of the eigenvalue μ_σ. Then the series

$$\sum_\sigma m_\sigma |\mu_\sigma|^2$$

must converge. This implies that if there exists an infinitude of eigenvalues, then $\mu_\sigma \to 0$. The only possible point of accumulation of the complex μ-values is the origin.

2. *Operators without Eigenvalues*

It can happen, of course, that the components determined by the eigenvalues do not completely characterize the operator in question, but that a residue operator without eigenvalues remains. Our previous considerations are then no longer applicable. We shall now examine more closely this case of completely continuous operators having no eigenvalues.

We again assume that $\mathfrak{H}' = \mathfrak{H}$. We can then form the sequence of powers $\mathfrak{K}\mathfrak{K}y = \mathfrak{K}^2 y, \cdots, \mathfrak{K}\mathfrak{K}^{n-1}y = \mathfrak{K}^n y$. All these operators are still completely continuous and for each we have $\mathfrak{H}' = \mathfrak{H}$. Furthermore, $\|\mathfrak{K}^n y\| \leqq \|\mathfrak{K}\|^n \cdot \|y\|$, and hence $\|\mathfrak{K}^n\| \leqq \|\mathfrak{K}\|^n$. This implies that for complex λ such that $|\lambda| \cdot \|\mathfrak{K}\| < 1$ the series

$$\|y\| + |\lambda| \, \|\mathfrak{K}y\| + |\lambda|^2 \|\mathfrak{K}^2 y\| + \cdots$$

is majorized by the convergent series $\|y\|(1 + |\lambda| \; \|\mathfrak{K}\| + |\lambda|^2 \; \|\mathfrak{K}\|^2 + \cdots)$ and hence for such λ the series

$$y + \lambda\mathfrak{K}y + \lambda^2\mathfrak{K}^2 y + \cdots$$

converges strongly to a certain element z in $\mathfrak{H}$.[15] This last series is called the Neumann series associated with $\mathfrak{K}$. We can readily see that

$$\lambda\mathfrak{K}z = \lambda\mathfrak{K}y + \lambda^2\mathfrak{K}^2 y + \cdots = z - y,$$

which tells us that for all y,

$$z - \lambda\mathfrak{K}z = y$$

has a solution z defined by the Neumann series. Hence, *no eigenvalue of the completely continuous operator $\mathfrak{K}$ can lie within the circle $|\lambda| = 1/\|\mathfrak{K}\|$.*

[15] $\|\sum_{i=n+1}^{m} \lambda^i \mathfrak{K}^i y\| \leqq (\sum_{i=n+1}^{m} |\lambda|^i \|\mathfrak{K}\|^i) \|y\| \to 0$ as $n, \; m \to \infty$. Hence $\sum_{i=1}^{n} \lambda^i \mathfrak{K}^i y$ is a Cauchy sequence, and as such it converges to some z in $\mathfrak{H}$. (Ed.)

Nevertheless, the true domain of convergence of the Neumann series can be larger than the circle of radius $1/\|\mathfrak{K}\|$. In any case, this domain is a circle in the complex plane, with radius $\mathfrak{R}(y)$ a function of y. It can be shown that the usual rules of operation with power series apply to our operator series. In particular, if the series converges for a certain λ_0, then it must converge for all λ such that $|\lambda| < |\lambda_0|$. Indeed, if we put $s_n = \sum_{\alpha=0}^{n} \lambda_0{}^\alpha \mathfrak{K}^\alpha y$ and $z_0 = \sum_{\alpha=0}^{\infty} \lambda_0{}^\alpha \mathfrak{K}^\alpha y$ and let $n \to \infty$, then

$$\|\lambda_0^n \mathfrak{K}^n y\| = \|s_n - s_{n-1}\| \leqq \|s_n - z_0\| + \|s_{n-1} - z_0\| \to 0.$$

Hence $\|\lambda_0{}^n \mathfrak{K}^n y\| \leqq C$ for all n, so that

$$\begin{aligned} &\|y\| + |\lambda|^1\|\mathfrak{K}y\| + \cdots + |\lambda|^n\|\mathfrak{K}^n y\| \\ &= \|y\| + \left|\frac{\lambda}{\lambda_0}\right| \cdot \|\lambda_0 \mathfrak{K} y\| + \cdots + \left|\frac{\lambda}{\lambda_0}\right|^n \cdot \|\lambda_0^n \mathfrak{K}^n y\| \\ &\leqq C\left(1 + \left|\frac{\lambda}{\lambda_0}\right| + \cdots + \left|\frac{\lambda}{\lambda_0}\right|^n\right) < \frac{C}{1 - |\lambda/\lambda_0|}. \end{aligned}$$

This tells us that $\sum_{\alpha=0}^{\infty} |\lambda|^\alpha \|\mathfrak{K}^\alpha y\|$ is convergent, as is the Neumann series for the λ in question. In particular, if $\lim_{n\to\infty} \sqrt[n]{\|\mathfrak{K}^n y\|} = 0$ for all y, then the Neumann series converges for all complex λ and for all y in $\mathfrak{H}$. *In such a case no eigenvalues exist*, for, by the Fredholm theorems, since the nonhomogeneous equation can be solved for all λ, we know that no nontrivial solution to the homogeneous equation can exist.

Conversely, let us now assume that the completely continuous operator $\mathfrak{K}$ possesses no eigenvalues. Then, using Fredholm's theorems, we conclude that the nonhomogeneous equation has a unique solution z for all y in $\mathfrak{H}$ and all complex λ. Hence, the operator

$$z = (\mathfrak{I} - \lambda\mathfrak{K})^{-1} y$$

exists for all y and all λ. For any fixed λ this operator is obviously bounded, for $(\mathfrak{I} - \lambda\mathfrak{K})^{-1*} = (\mathfrak{I} - \bar{\lambda}\mathfrak{K}^*)^{-1}$ exists for all y; and this, by §5, guarantees boundedness. In addition, this operator is a function of λ and, in any neighborhood of every λ_0 it can be expanded in a power series in $\lambda - \lambda_0$, namely,

$$\begin{aligned}(\mathfrak{I} - \lambda\mathfrak{K})^{-1}y &= (\mathfrak{I} - \lambda_0\mathfrak{K} - (\lambda - \lambda_0)\mathfrak{K})^{-1}y \\ &= (\mathfrak{I} - \lambda_0\mathfrak{K})^{-1}[\mathfrak{I} - (\lambda - \lambda_0)(\mathfrak{I} - \lambda_0\mathfrak{K})^{-1}\mathfrak{K}]^{-1}y \\ &= (\mathfrak{I} - \lambda_0\mathfrak{K})^{-1}[\mathfrak{I} + (\lambda - \lambda_0)(\mathfrak{I} - \lambda_0\mathfrak{K})^{-1}\mathfrak{K} \\ &\quad + (\lambda - \lambda_0)^2(\mathfrak{I} - \lambda_0\mathfrak{K})^{-2}\mathfrak{K}^2 + \cdots]y \\ &= \mathfrak{R}y.\end{aligned}$$

This series converges for $|\lambda - \lambda_0|M < 1$ provided that

$$\|(\mathfrak{I} - \lambda_0\mathfrak{K})^{-1}\mathfrak{K}y\| \leqq M\|y\|.$$

Naturally, $\mathfrak{R}$ commutes with $\mathfrak{I} - \lambda\mathfrak{K}$ and hence with $\mathfrak{K}$.

The general theory of analytic continuation of power series applied to the problem at hand tells us that the true domain of convergence of the Neumann series of a completely continuous operator $\mathfrak{K}$ without eigenvalues must be the whole plane. Indeed, any finite domain of convergence could be further extended by analytic continuation. Likewise, the series $\sum_{\alpha=0}^{\infty} |\lambda|^\alpha \cdot \|\mathfrak{K}^\alpha y\|$ is everywhere convergent. Therefore,

$$\lim_{n\to\infty} \sqrt[n]{\|\mathfrak{K}^n y\|} = 0.$$

In short, we have shown that *a necessary and sufficient condition for a completely continuous operator* $\mathfrak{K}$ *to have no eigenvalues is that*

$$\lim_{n\to\infty} \sqrt[n]{\|\mathfrak{K}^n y\|} = 0$$

for all y *in* $\mathfrak{H}$.

§11. Notes and Exercises to Chapter II

1. If the dimension of a Hilbert space is not infinite but rather some finite integer n, then we know that this Hilbert space is isomorphic to n-dimensional Euclidean space $\mathfrak{R}_n$. Any linear operator in $\mathfrak{R}_n$ can be represented by an $n \times n$ square matrix, and, conversely, every such matrix can be thought of as representing a linear operator. Every weakly convergent sequence can be shown to be strongly convergent, and all linear operators are necessarily completely continuous. We leave it to the reader to adapt all our previous theorems and proofs to the case of $\mathfrak{R}_n$.

2. We define the characteristic polynomial $p(\mu)$ of a matrix A by the equation

$$p(\mu) = \mathrm{Det}|\mu E - A| = \mu^n + p_1\mu^{n-1} + \cdots + p_n.$$

The coefficients $p(\mu)$ can be calculated from the relation

$$p_k = -\frac{1}{k}\sigma(AB_{k-1}) \qquad (k = 1, 2, \cdots, n).$$

where $\sigma(M)$ stands for the trace of the matrix M (i.e., the sum of the diagonal elements of M), $B_0 = E$, while B_k is recursively defined by $B_k = AB_{k-1} - (1/k)\sigma(AB_{k-1})E$. We must have $B_n = 0$. If $\mathrm{Det}|A| \neq 0$, then $A^{-1} = (1/p_n)B_{n-1}$. From

$$(\mu E - A)Q(\mu) = p(\mu)E$$

we can deduce that $Q(\mu) = \mu^{n-1}B_0 + \mu^{n-2}\cdot B_1 + \cdots + B_{n-1}$. We leave it to the reader to prove this result and use it to calculate the spectral decomposition of A.[16]

3. If T is a real matrix with nonzero determinant, then $P = TT'$ must be symmetric and positive definite. Hence we can always find a positive square root Q of P, $Q^2 = P$. Then $S = Q^{-1}T$ is orthogonal and $SS' = S'S = E$. If A and $T^{-1}AT = B$ are both orthogonal, then $S^{-1}AS = B$. Hence if the real orthogonal matrices A_i $(i = 1, 2, \cdots, k)$ can be transformed by means of the real matrix T into orthogonal matrices B_i, then the orthogonal matrix S can effect the same transformation as T. In the theory of crystal classes this result means that if two crystal classes are real equivalent then they are also real-orthogonal equivalent.

4. In the theory of probability one studies probability density functions $\varphi(x)$. These functions are defined over the

[16] Sourian, I. M., Une méthode pour la décomposition spectrale et l'inversion des matrices, *C. R. Paris* **227** (1948), 1010–1011.

interval $(-\infty, \infty)$, take on real values $\geqq 0$, and $\int_{-\infty}^{\infty} \varphi(x)\,dx = 1$. The best known example of such a function is the Gaussian distribution, or normal curve, defined by

$$\varphi(x) = \frac{h}{\sqrt{\pi}} \exp[-h^2(x-a)^2]$$

with a maximum at $x = a$. Let $\varphi_n(x)$ be a sequence of probability density functions which vanish at infinity sufficiently rapidly. Then the convolution

$$w(x) = \int_{-\infty}^{\infty} \varphi_1(x')\varphi_2(x-x')\,dx' = \int_{-\infty}^{\infty} \varphi_1(x-x')\varphi_2(x')\,dx'$$

is the probability distribution function for the random variable $x = x_1 + x_2$ in terms of the probability density functions of the independent random variables x_1 and x_2. With any probability density function $\varphi(x)$ for a random variable we associate its Fourier transform or characteristic function of the random variable:

$$\Phi(u) = \int_{-\infty}^{\infty} \varphi(x) e^{ixu}\,dx.$$

If $\Phi_1(u)$ and $\Phi_2(u)$ are the characteristic functions of $\varphi_1(x)$ and $\varphi_2(x)$, respectively, then the characteristic function of $w(x)$ is $\Phi_1(u)\cdot\Phi_2(u)$. Similarly, given random variables with probability density functions $\varphi_1(x), \cdots, \varphi_n(x)$, the characteristic function of their sum is the product $\Phi_1(u) \cdots \Phi_n(u)$. Now, if

$$\Phi(u) = \int_{-\infty}^{\infty} w(x) e^{ixu}\,dx,$$

then we have the inverse relation

$$w(x) = \frac{1}{2\pi}\int_{-\infty}^{\infty} \Phi(u) e^{-ixu}\,du.$$

The reader can prove this result by studying the operator

$$\mathfrak{R}w = \int_{-\infty}^{\infty} e^{ixu} w(x)\,dx$$

which can be shown to be bounded in $\mathfrak{L}_2(-\infty, \infty)$ and to have a bounded inverse

$$\mathfrak{K}^{-1}\Phi = \frac{1}{2\pi}\int_{-\infty}^{\infty} e^{-ixu}\Phi(u)\,du.$$

The heart of the proof lies in the Fourier integral formula $\varphi(x) = (1/2\pi)\int_{-\infty}^{\infty}\int_{-\infty}^{\infty} e^{i(x-y)u}\varphi(u)\,du\,dy$, which holds provided $\varphi(x)$ is continuous and of bounded variation and provided that $\int_{-\infty}^{\infty} |\varphi(x)|\,dx$ exists.

We leave it to the reader to show that, provided the conditions listed below are satisfied, the distribution of sums tends asymptotically to a Gaussian distribution. These conditions are

(1) The sum of the standard deviations $\int_{-\infty}^{\infty} |x - \alpha_k|^2 \varphi_k(x)\,dx$ of the given distributions tends to infinity with n (α_k is the mean of the distribution φ_k).

(2) The absolute third moments $\int_{-\infty}^{\infty} |x - \alpha_k|^3 \varphi_k(x)\,dx$ are bounded from above.

(3) The density functions $\varphi_k(x)$ are of uniformly bounded variation.

In proving the above theorem one again uses the Fourier transform to show that the product $\Phi_1(u) \cdots \Phi_n(u)$ tends to an exponential function as $n \to \infty$.

III. SPECTRAL THEORY

§12. Spectral Theory of Bounded Hermitian Operators

1. The Spectrum

If by the spectrum of a completely continuous Hermitian operator we merely mean the totality of its eigenvalues, then we can say that in §8 we brought the study of the spectral theory of such operators to a close and, in particular, gave a representation of such an operator in terms of its spectrum. The problem that now faces us is to examine to what extent we can develop an analogous spectral theory for arbitary, not necessarily completely continuous, Hermitian operators. The key to such a development lies in formulating an appropriate definition for the spectrum of such an operator. Note that for a completely continuous operator $\mathfrak{K}$ the associated operator $\mathfrak{I} - \lambda\mathfrak{K}$ has a unique and bounded inverse $(\mathfrak{I} - \lambda\mathfrak{K})^{-1}$ if and only if λ does not belong to the spectrum of $\mathfrak{K}$ (indeed, if λ is not an eigenvalue then the nonhomogeneous equation $(\mathfrak{I} - \lambda\mathfrak{K})y = x$, as well as the equation $(\mathfrak{I} - \lambda\mathfrak{K}^*)z = x$, can be solved for any x; hence $(\mathfrak{I} - \lambda\mathfrak{K})^{-1}x$ is defined for all x and so $(\mathfrak{I} - \lambda\mathfrak{K})^{-1}$ is bounded;[1] on the other hand, if λ is an eigenvalue, the inverse operator does not exist. We are thus led to define the spectrum of a bounded Hermitian operator $\mathfrak{K}$ as the totality of λ's for which the equation

$$y - \lambda\mathfrak{K}y = x$$

cannot be solved in $\mathfrak{H}$ for all x. What does the spectrum look like in this general case?

[1] Put $\mathfrak{I} - \lambda\mathfrak{K} = \mathfrak{M}$. $\mathfrak{M}^{-1}$ and $(\mathfrak{M}^*)^{-1}$ exist. If we could show the existence of $(\mathfrak{M}^{-1})^*$, then, by the theorem on p. 33, we could conclude that $\mathfrak{M}^{-1}$ is bounded. Now, $(\mathfrak{M}y, x) = (y, \mathfrak{M}^*x)$. If we rewrite this equality by putting $y = \mathfrak{M}^{-1}z$ and $x = (\mathfrak{M}^*)^{-1}u$, then we get $(z, (\mathfrak{M}^*)^{-1}u) = (\mathfrak{M}^{-1}z, \mathfrak{M}^*(\mathfrak{M}^*)^{-1}u) = (\mathfrak{M}^{-1}z, u)$; but this means that $(\mathfrak{M}^*)^{-1} = (\mathfrak{M}^{-1})^*$. (Ed.)

The main difference between this general case and the completely continuous case lies in the fact that we can no longer make use of the Fredholm theorems. These theorems were crucial in our proofs for the completely continuous case. Also crucial was the fact that for $\|y\| = 1$, $(\mathfrak{K}y, y)$ took on its maximum at a certain point y. This lemma cannot be utilized in the general case—for consider the bounded Hermitian operator $\mathfrak{K}$ defined over the Hilbert space of sequences by the matrix

$$\begin{pmatrix} \frac{1}{2} & 0 & 0 & \cdots \\ 0 & \frac{2}{3} & 0 & \cdots \\ 0 & 0 & \frac{3}{4} & \cdots \\ \cdot & \cdot & \cdot & \cdots \end{pmatrix}.$$

The least upper bound of $(\mathfrak{K}y, y)$ for $\|y\| = 1$ is obviously 1; yet at no point of this domain is this value attained, for we always have

$$\tfrac{1}{2}|y_1|^2 + \tfrac{2}{3}|y_2|^2 + \cdots < |y_1|^2 + |y_2|^2 + \cdots = 1.$$

We must therefore seek a completely new approach to our problem.[2]

First we establish the following result: *The spectrum of a bounded Hermitian operator can only consist of real numbers.* For suppose $\lambda = \lambda_1 + i\lambda_2, \lambda_2 \neq 0$, is a complex number belonging to the spectrum of such an operator. Then if $\mathfrak{A} = \mathfrak{I} - \lambda\mathfrak{K}$ we see that

$$\begin{aligned} \mathfrak{A}\mathfrak{A}^* = \mathfrak{A}^*\mathfrak{A} &= (\mathfrak{I} - (\lambda_1 + i\lambda_2)\mathfrak{K})(\mathfrak{I} - (\lambda_1 - i\lambda_2)\mathfrak{K}) \\ &= \mathfrak{I} - 2\lambda_1\mathfrak{K} + (\lambda_1^2 + \lambda_2^2)\mathfrak{K}^2 = (\mathfrak{I} - \lambda_1\mathfrak{K})^2 + \lambda_2^2\mathfrak{K}^2 \end{aligned}$$

is positive and Hermitian and we have

$$\begin{aligned} (\mathfrak{A}\mathfrak{A}^*y, y) &= ((\mathfrak{I} - \lambda_1\mathfrak{K})^2 y + \lambda_2^2\mathfrak{K}^2 y, y) \\ &= \|(\mathfrak{I} - \lambda_1\mathfrak{K})y\|^2 + \lambda_2^2\|\mathfrak{K}y\|^2. \end{aligned}$$

In this case the number m of §9 is positive. For if it were equal

[2] To see that $\mathfrak{K}$ defined by the above matrix is not completely continuous note that while $\mathfrak{e}_1, \mathfrak{e}_2, \cdots \rightharpoonup 0$, $\frac{1}{2}\mathfrak{e}_1, \frac{2}{3}\mathfrak{e}_2, \cdots$ does not converge strongly. (Ed.)

to zero there would exist a weakly convergent sequence y_n with $\|y_n\| = 1$ such that

$$(\mathfrak{A}\mathfrak{A}^* y_n, y_n) = \|(\mathfrak{I} - \lambda_1 \mathfrak{K})y_n\|^2 + \lambda_2^2 \|\mathfrak{K}y_n\|^2 \to 0,$$

whence $\|(\mathfrak{I} - \lambda_1 \mathfrak{K})y_n\| \to 0$ and also $\|\mathfrak{K}y_n\| \to 0$ (since $\lambda_2 \neq 0$). This would imply that $\|y_n\| \to 0$. This contradiction implies that $m > 0$, which tells us that $\mathfrak{I} - \lambda\mathfrak{K}$ has a unique and bounded inverse (cf. 2., §9). This means that for any x in $\mathfrak{H}$ the nonhomogeneous equation $(\mathfrak{I} - \lambda\mathfrak{K})y = x$ admits a unique solution y in $\mathfrak{H}$, i.e., λ cannot belong to the spectrum of $\mathfrak{K}$.

Our next problem is to characterize those sets of points on the λ axis which can serve as spectra. In the case of completely continuous operators the spectrum must be a discrete set of points admitting only infinity as a point of accumulation. For the spectrum of an arbitrary bounded $\mathfrak{K}$ we should expect a more general point set.

From now on we shall have to modify our notation somewhat. Let $\mu = 1/\lambda$ once again. We shall call the set of reciprocals of the λ the μ spectrum. Our operator equation now takes the form

$$\mu y - \mathfrak{K}y = x.$$

In the case of a completely continuous operator the μ spectrum is a countable, bounded point set, having zero as a point of accumulation.

We shall prove the following theorem: *If $\mathfrak{K}$ is a bounded Hermitian operator, then its μ spectrum is a bounded point set,* for suppose $|\mu| > \|\mathfrak{K}\|$. Then the operator series

$$\frac{x}{\mu} + \frac{\mathfrak{K}x}{\mu^2} + \frac{\mathfrak{K}^2 x}{\mu^3} + \cdots = \mathfrak{R}x$$

converges for all x in $\mathfrak{H}$ because the numerical series

$$\frac{\|x\|}{|\mu|}\left(1 + \frac{\|\mathfrak{K}\|}{|\mu|} + \frac{\|\mathfrak{K}\|^2}{|\mu|^2} + \cdots\right)$$

is convergent; the operator series above represents a bounded Hermitian operator. For $y = \mathfrak{R}x$

$$\mu y - x = \mathfrak{K}\left(\frac{x}{\mu} + \frac{\mathfrak{K}x}{\mu^2} + \cdots\right) = \mathfrak{K}\mathfrak{R}x = \mathfrak{K}y,$$

which shows that our original operator equation has a solution for any x. Hence μ cannot belong to the spectrum. This shows that *the μ spectrum of a bounded Hermitian operator lies on the segment* $-\|\mathfrak{K}\| \leqq \mu \leqq \|\mathfrak{K}\|$.

2. Projection Operators and Spectral Families

In developing the spectral theory of operators we shall rely on the concept of the square root of a positive Hermitian operator already discussed in §9 and on the concept of a projection operator which was first introduced at the end of §3 and which we are about to investigate in greater detail. Thus, let $\mathfrak{P}$ be a bounded Hermitian operator such that $\mathfrak{P}^2 = \mathfrak{P}$. The set of all elements h in $\mathfrak{H}$ for which $\mathfrak{P}h = h$ forms a linear manifold which, by the continuity of $\mathfrak{P}$, satisfies axioms (a), (b), (c). This means that the set of all such h is a subspace $\mathfrak{M}$ of $\mathfrak{H}$. For any y in $\mathfrak{H}$, $\mathfrak{P}y = \mathfrak{P}(\mathfrak{P}y) = h$ is an element of $\mathfrak{M}$. If $y = h + g$, then $\mathfrak{P}g = 0$. If we denote by $\mathfrak{N}$ the kernel of $\mathfrak{P}$, i.e., the set of all x in $\mathfrak{H}$ for which $\mathfrak{P}x = 0$, then we have, as in §3, $\mathfrak{H} = \mathfrak{M} \oplus \mathfrak{N}$. Moreover, $(h, g) = (\mathfrak{P}h, g) = (h, \mathfrak{P}g) = 0$. Hence $\mathfrak{P}$ is the orthogonal projection from $\mathfrak{H}$ onto $\mathfrak{M}$ while, conversely, for every such orthogonal projection from $\mathfrak{H}$ onto a subspace $\mathfrak{M}$ the associated operator $\mathfrak{P}$ must map any y onto an h in $\mathfrak{M}$, $\mathfrak{P}y = h$. Since $\mathfrak{P}h = h$, we see that $\mathfrak{P}^2y = \mathfrak{P}y$, hence $\mathfrak{P}^2 = \mathfrak{P}$, while if $y = h + g$, then $\mathfrak{P}g = 0$ and, since our projection has been assumed orthogonal, $(h, g) = 0$. This implies $(\mathfrak{P}y, g) = 0$, $(\mathfrak{P}y, y) = (\mathfrak{P}y, h) = (y, \mathfrak{P}^*y) = (y, \mathfrak{P}h) = (y, h) = (y, \mathfrak{P}y)$. Hence $\mathfrak{P}^*y = \mathfrak{P}y$ and $\mathfrak{P}^* = \mathfrak{P}$.[3] If we do not impose

[3] It is clear that an operator $\mathfrak{A}$ on $\mathfrak{H}$ is 0 if and only if $(\mathfrak{A}x, y) = 0$ for all x, y in $\mathfrak{H}$. If $\mathfrak{H}$ is a (complex) Hilbert space, then we can show that $\mathfrak{A} = 0$ if and only if $(\mathfrak{A}x, x) = 0$ for all x in $\mathfrak{H}$. Indeed, let $(\mathfrak{A}x, x) = 0$ for all x in $\mathfrak{H}$. Then $0 = (\mathfrak{A}(\alpha x + \beta y), \alpha x + \beta y) = |\alpha|^2(\mathfrak{A}x, x) + |\beta|^2(\mathfrak{A}y, y) + \alpha\bar{\beta}(\mathfrak{A}x, y) + \bar{\alpha}\beta(\mathfrak{A}y, x)$. Putting $\alpha = \beta = 1$ we find $0 = (\mathfrak{A}x, y) + (\mathfrak{A}y, x)$. Putting $\alpha = i$, $\beta = 1$, we find $0 = i(\mathfrak{A}x, y) - i(\mathfrak{A}y, x)$, or $(\mathfrak{A}x, y) - (\mathfrak{A}y, x) = 0$. It follows that $(\mathfrak{A}x, y) = 0$ and thus $\mathfrak{A} = 0$.

We quote this result because the author uses it to prove that $\mathfrak{P} = \mathfrak{P}^*$ and uses it again on p. 104. That $\mathfrak{P} = \mathfrak{P}^*$ can be proved directly as follows: Let $y = h + g$, $y' = h' + g'$. Then $(\mathfrak{P}y, y') = (\mathfrak{P}h, y') = (h, h' + g') = (h, h') = (h + g, h') = (y, \mathfrak{P}y')$, that is, $\mathfrak{P} = \mathfrak{P}^*$. (Ed.)

the above orthogonality condition we can still define an operator S for which $S^2 = S$; we call such an operator an oblique projection.

Let $\mathfrak{K}$ be an arbitrary bounded Hermitian operator. Then $\mathfrak{K}^2$ must be a positive Hermitian operator, since $(\mathfrak{K}^2 y, y) = \|\mathfrak{K}y\|^2 \geqq 0$ for all y. We indicate the positive character of $\mathfrak{K}^2$ by writing $\mathfrak{K}^2 \geqq 0$. Following the procedure described in §9, we extract the positive square root $\mathfrak{L}$ of $\mathfrak{K}^2$. We put

$$\mathfrak{K}_+ = \tfrac{1}{2}(\mathfrak{L} + \mathfrak{K}), \qquad \mathfrak{K}_- = \tfrac{1}{2}(\mathfrak{L} - \mathfrak{K}), \qquad \mathfrak{K} = \mathfrak{K}_+ - \mathfrak{K}_-$$

and call $\mathfrak{K}_+$ the positive part of $\mathfrak{K}$ and $\mathfrak{K}_-$ its negative part. If $\mathfrak{K}$ itself happens to be positive, then $\mathfrak{L} = \mathfrak{K}$ and $\mathfrak{K} = \mathfrak{K}_+$, $\mathfrak{K}_- = 0$.

Let us now consider the set $\mathfrak{M}$ of all those elements h in $\mathfrak{H}$ for which $\mathfrak{K}_+ h = 0$. This set forms a subspace in $\mathfrak{H}$. Let $\mathfrak{P} = \mathfrak{P}^*$ denote the orthogonal projection from $\mathfrak{H}$ onto $\mathfrak{M}$. Then $\mathfrak{P}y = h$ belongs to $\mathfrak{M}$ and $\mathfrak{K}_+\mathfrak{P}y = 0$ for all y in $\mathfrak{H}$, i.e., $\mathfrak{K}_+\mathfrak{P} = 0$.

Since $\mathfrak{L}$ commutes with all operators which themselves commute with $\mathfrak{K}^2$ (in symbols: $\mathfrak{L}$ cc $\mathfrak{K}^2$), we also have $\mathfrak{L}$ cc $\mathfrak{K}$ (since every operator which commutes with $\mathfrak{K}$ also commutes with $\mathfrak{K}^2$), so that $\mathfrak{K}_+$ cc $\mathfrak{K}$ and $\mathfrak{K}_-$ cc $\mathfrak{K}$. We now prove that $\mathfrak{P}$ cc $\mathfrak{K}$. Suppose that $\mathfrak{O}$ commutes with $\mathfrak{K}$. Then $\mathfrak{O}$ c $\mathfrak{K}_+$. The equation $\mathfrak{K}_+ \mathfrak{O}y = \mathfrak{O}\mathfrak{K}_+ y$ shows that $\mathfrak{O}h$ lies in $\mathfrak{M}$ for h in $\mathfrak{M}$. This implies that $\mathfrak{O}\mathfrak{P}y = \mathfrak{P}\mathfrak{O}\mathfrak{P}y$ for all y in $\mathfrak{H}$, i.e., $\mathfrak{O}\mathfrak{P} = \mathfrak{P}\mathfrak{O}\mathfrak{P}$. If we repeat this argument with $\mathfrak{O}^*$ in place of $\mathfrak{O}$ we get $\mathfrak{P}\mathfrak{O} = \mathfrak{P}\mathfrak{O}\mathfrak{P} = \mathfrak{O}\mathfrak{P}$, i.e., $\mathfrak{O}$ c $\mathfrak{P}$, as asserted.

Moreover, $\mathfrak{L}$ c $\mathfrak{K}$ implies that $\mathfrak{K}_+\mathfrak{K}_- = \tfrac{1}{4}(\mathfrak{L}^2 - \mathfrak{K}^2) = 0$. Hence all elements $\mathfrak{K}_- y$ belong to $\mathfrak{M}$ and $\mathfrak{P}\mathfrak{K}_- y = \mathfrak{K}_- y$; $\mathfrak{P}\mathfrak{K}_- = \mathfrak{K}_-$. Since $\mathfrak{P}$, $\mathfrak{K}_+$ and $\mathfrak{K}_-$ commute with each other, we have

$$\mathfrak{P}\mathfrak{K}_- = \mathfrak{K}_-\mathfrak{P} = \mathfrak{K}_-, \qquad \mathfrak{P}\mathfrak{K}_+ = \mathfrak{K}_+\mathfrak{P} = 0,$$

and therefore

$$\mathfrak{K}\mathfrak{P} = \mathfrak{P}\mathfrak{K} = -\mathfrak{K}_-, \qquad \mathfrak{K}(\mathfrak{I} - \mathfrak{P}) = \mathfrak{K} + \mathfrak{K}_- = \mathfrak{K}_+.$$

Furthermore, $\mathfrak{K}_+ + \mathfrak{K}_- = \mathfrak{L} \geqq 0$. This implies that $\mathfrak{K}_- =$

$\mathfrak{P}\mathfrak{K}_- + \mathfrak{P}\mathfrak{K}_+ = \mathfrak{P}\mathfrak{L} = \mathfrak{L}\mathfrak{P} \geqq 0$, since $(\mathfrak{L}\mathfrak{P}y, y) = (\mathfrak{L}\mathfrak{P}^2 y, y) = (\mathfrak{P}\mathfrak{L}\mathfrak{P}y, y) = (\mathfrak{L}\mathfrak{P}y, \mathfrak{P}y) \geqq 0$. Thus $\mathfrak{K}_-$ is positive. Similarly,

$$\mathfrak{K}_+ = \mathfrak{L} - \mathfrak{K}_- = \mathfrak{L} - \mathfrak{P}\mathfrak{L} = (\mathfrak{I} - \mathfrak{P})\mathfrak{L}$$

is $\geqq 0$ for $\mathfrak{I} - \mathfrak{P}$ is a projection (because $(\mathfrak{I} - \mathfrak{P})^2 = \mathfrak{I} - 2\mathfrak{P} + \mathfrak{P} = \mathfrak{I} - \mathfrak{P}$). Hence, *the positive and negative parts of* $\mathfrak{K}$ *must both be positive.*

Let us use completely continuous operators to illustrate the above results. We recall (cf. §8) that a completely continuous Hermitian operator can be represented in $\mathfrak{H}_0$ by a diagonal matrix whose nonzero diagonal entries are the (positive and negative) values of the μ spectrum (note the change of notation relative to §8). The operator $\mathfrak{K}_+$ is now represented by a diagonal matrix which retains the positive diagonal entries of $\mathfrak{K}$ and has zeros elsewhere, and the operator $\mathfrak{K}_-$ is represented by a diagonal matrix which retains the absolute values of the negative entries of $\mathfrak{K}$ and has zeros elsewhere. The operator $\mathfrak{P}$ is represented by a matrix obtained from the matrix of $\mathfrak{K}_+$ by replacing its positive diagonal entries by zeros and its zero diagonal entries by ones. Thus theoretical considerations have led us to a way of separating positive and negative μ values, independently of any particular representation of our operator.

We propose to advance our theory by applying the above tools not to $\mathfrak{K}$ but rather to $\mathfrak{K}_\mu = \mathfrak{K} - \mu\mathfrak{I}$, μ real but otherwise arbitrary. As above, we can define $\mathfrak{L}_\mu$, $\mathfrak{K}_{\mu+}$, $\mathfrak{K}_{\mu-}$, $\mathfrak{P}_\mu$ and the set $\mathfrak{M}_\mu$. We must have $\mathfrak{L}_\mu$ cc $\mathfrak{K}_\mu$, $\mathfrak{K}_{\mu+}$ cc $\mathfrak{K}_\mu$, etc. We therefore also have $\mathfrak{L}_\mu$ cc $\mathfrak{K}$, $\mathfrak{K}_{\mu+}$ cc $\mathfrak{K}$, etc., and all the operators $\mathfrak{K}_\mu$, $\mathfrak{L}_\nu$, $\mathfrak{K}_{\rho+}$, $\mathfrak{K}_{\sigma-}$ $\mathfrak{P}_\tau$, with $\mu, \nu, \rho, \sigma, \tau$ real but otherwise arbitrary, must commute with each other.

We now focus our attention on the family of projection operators $\mathfrak{P}_\mu$. We call this family the spectral family of $\mathfrak{K}$ and propose to study its properties.

First and foremost, note that always $\mathfrak{P}_\mu\mathfrak{P}_\nu = \mathfrak{P}_\nu\mathfrak{P}_\mu$. We shall now show that

$$\mathfrak{P}_\mu \leqq \mathfrak{P}_\nu \qquad \text{for} \quad \mu \leqq \nu$$

(this means, of course, that $\mathfrak{P}_\nu - \mathfrak{P}_\mu \geqq 0$, i.e., this difference is positive). In fact

$$\mathfrak{K}_{\mu+} - \mathfrak{K}_{\nu+} + \mathfrak{K}_{\nu-} \geqq \mathfrak{K}_{\mu+} - \mathfrak{K}_{\nu+} + \mathfrak{K}_{\nu-} - \mathfrak{K}_{\mu-} = \mathfrak{K}_\mu - \mathfrak{K}_\nu \geqq 0.$$

This and the fact that $\mathfrak{K}_{\nu+} \geqq 0$ imply that

$$\mathfrak{K}_{\nu+}(\mathfrak{K}_{\mu+} - \mathfrak{K}_{\nu+} + \mathfrak{K}_{\nu-}) \geqq 0.$$

Indeed, from $\mathfrak{A} \geqq 0$ and $\mathfrak{B} \geqq 0$ and $\mathfrak{A}\mathfrak{B} = \mathfrak{B}\mathfrak{A}$ ($\mathfrak{A} = \mathfrak{A}^*$, $\mathfrak{B} = \mathfrak{B}^*$) it follows that $(\mathfrak{A}\mathfrak{B}y, y) \geqq 0$. In fact, let $\mathfrak{W}$ denote the positive $\sqrt{\mathfrak{A}}$. Then

$$(\mathfrak{U}\mathfrak{B}y, y) = (\mathfrak{W}^2\mathfrak{B}y, y) = (\mathfrak{W}\mathfrak{B}\mathfrak{M}y, y) = (\mathfrak{B}\mathfrak{W}y, \mathfrak{W}y) \geqq 0.$$

Now, using the fact that $\mathfrak{K}_{\nu+}\mathfrak{K}_{\nu-} = 0$ we see that

$$\begin{aligned}\|\mathfrak{K}_{\mu+}y\|^2 = (\mathfrak{K}_{\mu+}^2 y, y) &\geqq (\mathfrak{K}_{\nu+}\mathfrak{K}_{\mu+}y, y) \geqq (\mathfrak{K}_{\nu+}\mathfrak{K}_{\nu+}y, y)\\ &= \|\mathfrak{K}_{\nu+}y\|^2.\end{aligned}$$

Hence if $\mathfrak{K}_{\mu+}y = 0$, then also $\mathfrak{K}_{\nu+}y = 0$. Thus the set $\mathfrak{M}_\nu$ contains the set of elements $\mathfrak{M}_\mu$ and $\mathfrak{P}_\nu\mathfrak{P}_\mu y$ is the same as $\mathfrak{P}_\mu y$, i.e.,

$$\mathfrak{P}_\nu\mathfrak{P}_\mu = \mathfrak{P}_\mu\mathfrak{P}_\nu = \mathfrak{P}_\mu \qquad (\mu \leqq \nu).$$

Since $\mathfrak{J} - \mathfrak{P}_\mu \geqq 0$ and $\mathfrak{P}_\nu \geqq 0$, we must have

$$\mathfrak{P}_\nu - \mathfrak{P}_\mu = \mathfrak{P}_\nu - \mathfrak{P}_\mu\mathfrak{P}_\nu = (\mathfrak{J} - \mathfrak{P}_\mu)\mathfrak{P}_\nu \geqq 0.$$

Thus the family of projection operators $\mathfrak{P}_\mu$ is monotonically increasing with μ.

We shall denote the least upper bound and greatest lower bound of $(\mathfrak{K}y, y)$ when $\|y\| = 1$ by m and M, respectively. We claim that *if $\mu < m$ then* $\mathfrak{P}_\mu = 0$. First note that in this case $\mathfrak{K}_\mu = \mathfrak{K} - \mu\mathfrak{J}$ is always $\geqq 0$, for $(\mathfrak{K}y, y) \geqq \mu(y, y)$. Hence $\mathfrak{K}_{\mu+} = \mathfrak{K}_\mu$, $\mathfrak{K}_{\mu-} = 0$. From $(\mathfrak{K}_\mu y, y) \geqq (m - \mu)(y, y)$ it follows that $\mathfrak{K}_\mu y = \mathfrak{K}_{\mu+}y = 0$ if and only if $y = 0$. Hence $\mathfrak{P}_\mu = 0$, as asserted.

We further claim that $\mathfrak{P}_\mu = \mathfrak{J}$ for $\mu > M$. For in this case we have $-\mathfrak{K}_\mu = \mu\mathfrak{J} - \mathfrak{K} \geqq 0$, hence $\mathfrak{L}_\mu = -\mathfrak{K}_\mu$, $\mathfrak{K}_{\mu+} = 0$ and therefore $\mathfrak{P}_\mu = \mathfrak{J}$.

Finally we prove that $\mathfrak{P}_\mu$, as a function of the parameter μ, is continuous from the right.

To this end, let us form $\mathfrak{P}_\nu - \mathfrak{P}_\mu$ where $\nu > \mu$. Now let us keep μ fixed and let ν tend to μ. We shall show that under these hypotheses $\mathfrak{P}_\nu - \mathfrak{P}_\mu = \mathfrak{D}_\nu$ tends to a projection operator $\mathfrak{D}(\mu)$, i.e., there exists a projection operator $\mathfrak{D}(\mu)$ such that for every decreasing sequence of numbers $\nu_1, \nu_2, \cdots$ converging to μ and for every y in $\mathfrak{H}$ we have $\mathfrak{D}_{\nu_m} y \rightarrow \mathfrak{D}(\mu)y$. Note that the monotonicity property of the $\mathfrak{P}_\nu$ implies that $\mathfrak{D}_\nu \geqq 0$ and is monotonically decreasing as $\nu \rightarrow \mu$ (from the right). Similarly, for an arbitrary monotonically decreasing sequence ν_m with $\nu_m \rightarrow \mu$ the operators $(\mathfrak{D}_{\nu_n} - \mathfrak{D}_{\nu_m})\mathfrak{D}_{\nu_n}$ and $\mathfrak{D}_{\nu_m}(\mathfrak{D}_{\nu_n} - \mathfrak{D}_{\nu_m})$ are $\geqq 0$ provided that $m > n$. Therefore

$$(\mathfrak{D}^2_{\nu_n} y, y) \geqq (\mathfrak{D}_{\nu_m}\mathfrak{D}_{\nu_n} y, y) \geqq (\mathfrak{D}^2_{\nu_m} y, y).$$

Hence the sequence of numbers $(\mathfrak{D}^2_{\nu_n} y, y)$ has a limit independent of y and $(\mathfrak{D}_{\nu_m}\mathfrak{D}_{\nu_n} y, y)$ tends to this limit as $n, m \rightarrow \infty$. This implies that

$$\|(\mathfrak{D}_{\nu_m} - \mathfrak{D}_{\nu_n})y\|^2 = ((\mathfrak{D}_{\nu_m} - \mathfrak{D}_{\nu_n})^2 y, y)$$
$$= (\mathfrak{D}^2_{\nu_m} y, y) - 2(\mathfrak{D}_{\nu_m}\mathfrak{D}_{\nu_n} y, y) + (\mathfrak{D}^2_{\nu_n} y, y) \rightarrow 0,$$

which proves that the sequence $\mathfrak{D}_{\nu_n} y$ converges strongly to a limit $\mathfrak{D}(\mu)y$; hence $\mathfrak{D}(\mu)$ is defined for all y, is bounded, and is equal to its adjoint.[4] Since $\mathfrak{D}_\nu{}^2 = \mathfrak{P}_\nu{}^2 - 2\mathfrak{P}_\nu\mathfrak{P}_\mu + \mathfrak{P}_\mu{}^2 = \mathfrak{D}_\nu$, we see that $\mathfrak{D}^2(\mu) = \mathfrak{D}(\mu)$, i.e., $\mathfrak{D}(\mu)$ is a projection operator. This proves the existence of $\lim_{\nu \rightarrow \mu + 0}(\mathfrak{P}_\nu - \mathfrak{P}_\mu) = \mathfrak{D}(\mu)$. *We shall now show that* $\mathfrak{D}(\mu) = 0$. First notice that, for $\nu > \mu$, we always have

$$(*) \qquad \mu(\mathfrak{P}_\nu - \mathfrak{P}_\mu) \leqq \mathfrak{K}(\mathfrak{P}_\nu - \mathfrak{P}_\mu) \leqq \nu(\mathfrak{P}_\nu - \mathfrak{P}_\mu).$$

In fact

$$(\nu\mathfrak{I} - \mathfrak{K})(\mathfrak{P}_\nu - \mathfrak{P}_\mu) = -\mathfrak{K}_\nu(\mathfrak{P}_\nu - \mathfrak{P}_\mu) = -\mathfrak{K}_\nu\mathfrak{P}_\nu(\mathfrak{P}_\nu - \mathfrak{P}_\mu)$$
$$= \mathfrak{K}_{\nu^-}(\mathfrak{P}_\nu - \mathfrak{P}_\mu),$$

[4] $\mathfrak{D}$ is bounded because it is the limit of a sequence of bounded operators (cf. footnote on p. 51). To prove that $\mathfrak{D}^* = \mathfrak{D}$, we note that if $\mathfrak{A}_n$ is a sequence of bounded operators converging to a (necessarily bounded) operator $\mathfrak{A}$, then $\mathfrak{A}_n{}^* \rightarrow \mathfrak{A}^*$. Indeed, $(\mathfrak{A}_n y, z) \rightarrow (\mathfrak{A}y, z) = (y, \mathfrak{A}^* z)$ and $(\mathfrak{A}_n y, z) = (y, \mathfrak{A}_n{}^* z) \rightarrow (y, \mathfrak{B}z)$ imply that $\mathfrak{A}_n{}^* \rightarrow \mathfrak{B} = \mathfrak{A}^*$. (Ed.)

and this expression must be $\geqq 0$, because $\mathfrak{K}_{\nu^-} \geqq 0$ and $\mathfrak{P}_\nu - \mathfrak{P}_\mu \geqq 0$. This proves the right side of the inequality in question. Similarly, we have

$$(\mathfrak{K} - \mu\mathfrak{J})(\mathfrak{P}_\nu - \mathfrak{P}_\mu) = \mathfrak{K}_\mu(\mathfrak{P}_\nu - \mathfrak{P}_\mu) = \mathfrak{K}_\mu(\mathfrak{J} - \mathfrak{P}_\mu)(\mathfrak{P}_\nu - \mathfrak{P}_\mu)$$
$$= \mathfrak{K}_{\mu^+}(\mathfrak{P}_\nu - \mathfrak{P}_\mu) \geqq 0,$$

which proves the left side of this inequality.

If we now let $\nu \to \mu$, we see that

$$\mu\mathfrak{Q}(\mu) \leqq \mathfrak{K}_\mu\mathfrak{Q}(\mu) \leqq \mu\mathfrak{Q}(\mu),$$

i.e., $\mu\mathfrak{Q}(\mu) = \mathfrak{K}\mathfrak{Q}(\mu)$; $\mathfrak{K}_\mu\mathfrak{Q}(\mu) = 0$. Since $\mathfrak{K}_{\mu^+} = \mathfrak{K}_\mu(\mathfrak{J} - \mathfrak{P}_\mu)$ we have $\mathfrak{K}_{\mu^+}\mathfrak{Q}(\mu) = \mathfrak{K}_\mu\mathfrak{Q}(\mu)(\mathfrak{J} - \mathfrak{P}_\mu) = 0$. Hence, for all y, $\mathfrak{Q}(\mu)y$ is contained in $\mathfrak{M}_\mu$ and therefore $\mathfrak{P}_\mu\mathfrak{Q}(\mu) = \mathfrak{Q}(\mu)$. But on the other hand, $\mathfrak{P}_\nu - \mathfrak{P}_\mu = (\mathfrak{J} - \mathfrak{P}_\mu)(\mathfrak{P}_\nu - \mathfrak{P}_\mu)$ and hence, as $\nu \to \mu$ we obtain: $\mathfrak{Q}(\mu) = (\mathfrak{J} - \mathfrak{P}_\mu)\mathfrak{Q}(\mu) = 0$. This proves continuity from the right. Thus *the spectral family* $\mathfrak{P}_\mu$ *of* $\mathfrak{K}$ *has the following properties*:

1. $\mathfrak{P}_\mu \leqq \mathfrak{P}_\nu$ for $\mu \leqq \nu$,
2. $\mathfrak{P}_\nu\mathfrak{P}_\mu = \mathfrak{P}_\mu\mathfrak{P}_\nu = \mathfrak{P}_\mu$ for $\mu \leqq \nu$,
3. $\mathfrak{P}_{\mu+0} = \mathfrak{P}_\mu$,
4. $\lim_{\mu\to-\infty} \mathfrak{P}_\mu = 0$, $\lim_{\mu\to\infty} \mathfrak{P}_\mu = \mathfrak{J}$. In particular, $\mathfrak{P}_\mu = 0$ for $\mu < m$, $\mathfrak{P}_\mu = \mathfrak{J}$ for $\mu > M$.

For a better grasp of the meaning of the concept of the spectral family we consider the familiar case of a completely continuous self-adjoint operator $\mathfrak{K}$. For arbitrary μ, $\mathfrak{K}_{\mu^+}$ denotes the diagonal matrix which coincides with the diagonal matrix for $\mathfrak{K}_\mu$ whenever $\mu_\alpha > \mu$ and has zeros for the other diagonal entries, and $\mathfrak{K}_{\mu^-}$ denotes the diagonal matrix which coincides with the diagonal matrix for $-\mathfrak{K}_\mu$ whenever $\mu_\alpha \leqq \mu$ and has zeros for the other diagonal positions. Then $\mathfrak{P}_\mu$ is the diagonal matrix which contains zeros wherever $\mathfrak{K}_{\mu^+}$ has non-zero diagonal entries and ones for the other diagonal entries. These representations imply all the properties of the spectral family $\mathfrak{P}_\mu$ including continuity from the right. We see also that $\mathfrak{P}_\mu$ has a jump discontinuity at each μ_α. The origin is a point of accumulation of these points of discontinuity. Now consider a partition of $(-\infty, \infty)$. For each interval $(\nu_\kappa, \nu_{\kappa+1})$ of our partition we have (cf. p. 87):

$$\nu_\kappa(\mathfrak{P}_{\nu_{\kappa+1}} - \mathfrak{P}_{\nu_\kappa}) \leqq \mathfrak{K}(\mathfrak{P}_{\nu_{\kappa+1}} - \mathfrak{P}_{\nu_\kappa}) \leqq \nu_{\kappa+1}(\mathfrak{P}_{\nu_{\kappa+1}} - \mathfrak{P}_{\nu_\kappa}).$$

Note that if both ν_κ and $\nu_{\kappa+1}$ are outside the interval $(m, \|\mathfrak{K}\|)$, then the right and left sides in this double inequality reduce to zero. Summation of the remaining finitely many terms yields

$$\sum \nu_\kappa(\mathfrak{P}_{\nu_{\kappa+1}} - \mathfrak{P}_{\nu_\kappa}) \leqq \mathfrak{K} \leqq \sum \nu_{\kappa+1}(\mathfrak{P}_{\nu_{\kappa+1}} - \mathfrak{P}_{\nu_\kappa}).$$

(Here we made use of the fact that $\sum (\mathfrak{P}_{\nu_{\kappa-1}} - \mathfrak{P}_{\nu_\kappa}) = \mathfrak{I}$.) Only in the case where the interval $(\nu_\kappa, \nu_{\kappa+1})$ contains at least one μ_α do we get a summand different from zero on the left or right side of the last inequality. If our partition is refined indefinitely we obtain in the limit the representation

$$\mathfrak{K} = \sum_{\alpha=1}^{\infty} \mu_\alpha \mathfrak{O}_\alpha$$

involving all the μ_α. Each $\mathfrak{O}_\alpha$ is represented by a diagonal matrix of ones and zeros, and the number of ones is equal to the finite multiplicity of μ_α. We are thus led back to the familiar representation of $\mathfrak{K}$. In what follows we shall further study the above passage to the limit. In the case we have just studied this passage gave us no new results. We shall see what results it does lead to in the more general case of a bounded self-adjoint operator.

3. *Integrals over a Spectral Family*

We see that many considerations lead us to try to formulate the notion of integration of operators using the notion of the spectral family $\mathfrak{P}_\mu$. With this aim in mind, we associate with every interval $(a, b) = \delta$, a projection $\mathfrak{P}(\delta)$. Specifically, if the left and the right end point belong to the interval then $\mathfrak{P}(\delta) = \mathfrak{P}_b - \mathfrak{P}_{a-0}$;[5] if the right but not the left end point belongs to the interval then $\mathfrak{P}(\delta) = \mathfrak{P}_b - \mathfrak{P}_a$; if the left but not the right

[5] The existence of $\mathfrak{P}_{a-0}$ follows from an argument similar to that used in establishing the existence of $\mathfrak{P}_{a+0}$. (Ed.)

end point belongs to the interval then $\mathfrak{P}(\delta) = \mathfrak{P}_{b-0} - \mathfrak{P}_{a-0}$; and if neither end point belongs to the interval, then $\mathfrak{P}(\delta) = \mathfrak{P}_{b-0} - \mathfrak{P}_{a}$. If we have two different intervals with no point in common, then by property 2 in the definition of a spectral family we see that the product of the (obviously commutative) $\mathfrak{P}(\delta)$ associated with these intervals is zero. If we decompose δ into a finite or denumerable number of pairwise disjoint intervals $\delta_1, \delta_2, \cdots$, then $\mathfrak{P}(\delta)y = \sum \mathfrak{P}(\delta_\kappa)y$. If this sum is infinite it will converge for each y since $\sum_{\kappa=n+1}^{m} \mathfrak{P}(\delta_\kappa)y = \mathfrak{P}(\delta_{n+1} + \cdots + \delta_m)y$; as $m, n \to \infty$ this interval tends to zero and hence, by Bessel's inequality, we get $\| \mathfrak{P}(\delta_{n+1} + \cdots + \delta_m)y\| \to 0$.[6]

Let us now consider a bounded step function $F(\mu)$ defined on the real line, i.e., a function for which there exists a partition of the real line into a finite or denumerably infinite number of disjoint intervals δ_κ such that $F(\mu) = c_\kappa$ on δ_κ and $|c_\kappa| \leqq M_0$ for all κ. Observe that this definition admits partitions which include points other than the points of discontinuity of $F(\mu)$. We claim that $\sum_{\kappa=1}^{\infty} c_\kappa \mathfrak{P}(\delta_\kappa)$ converges. In fact, by the orthogonality of the $\mathfrak{P}(\delta_\kappa)$, we have

$$\left\| \sum_{\kappa=n+1}^{m} c_\kappa \mathfrak{P}(\delta_\kappa)y \right\|^2 = \sum_{\kappa=n+1}^{m} |c_\kappa|^2 \|\mathfrak{P}(\delta_\kappa)y\|^2 \leqq M_0^2 \sum_{\kappa=n+1}^{m} \|\mathfrak{P}(\delta_\kappa)y\|^2$$
$$= M_0^2 \left\{ \left\| \sum_{\kappa=1}^{m} \mathfrak{P}(\delta_\kappa)y \right\|^2 - \left\| \sum_{\kappa=1}^{n} \mathfrak{P}(\delta_\kappa)y \right\|^2 \right\};$$

and since $\sum_{\kappa=1}^{\infty} \mathfrak{P}(\delta_\kappa) = \mathfrak{J}$, we see that the right side above tends to zero as $m, n \to \infty$. Furthermore, $\left\|\sum_{\kappa=1}^{\infty} c_\kappa \mathfrak{P}(\delta_\kappa)\right\|$ has M_0 as upper bound, because

$$\left\| \sum_{\kappa=1}^{\infty} c_\kappa \mathfrak{P}(\delta_\kappa)y \right\|^2 = \lim_{n\to\infty} \left\| \sum_{\kappa=1}^{n} c_\kappa \mathfrak{P}(\delta_\kappa)y \right\|^2$$
$$= \lim_{n\to\infty} \sum_{\kappa=1}^{n} |c_\kappa|^2 \cdot \|\mathfrak{P}(\delta_\kappa)y\|^2$$
$$\leqq M_0^2 \lim_{n\to\infty} \sum_{\kappa=1}^{n} \|\mathfrak{P}(\delta_\kappa)y\|^2 = M_0^2 \|y\|^2.$$

[6] Note that $\|\sum_{\varkappa=1}^{m} \mathfrak{P}(\delta_\varkappa)y\|^2 = \sum_{\varkappa=1}^{m} \|\mathfrak{P}(\delta_\varkappa)y\|^2 \leqq \|y\|^2$, which implies that $\sum_{\varkappa=1}^{\infty} \|\mathfrak{P}(\delta_\varkappa)y\|^2$ converges. But then $\sum_{\varkappa=1}^{\infty} \mathfrak{P}(\delta_\varkappa)y = \sum_{\varkappa=1}^{\infty} \|\mathfrak{P}(\delta_\varkappa)y\| (\mathfrak{P}(\delta_\varkappa)y/\|\mathfrak{P}(\delta_\varkappa)y\|)$ is in $\mathfrak{H}$. (Ed.)

We can now define the integral of a step function $F(\mu)$ over the spectral family $\mathfrak{P}_\mu$:

$$F(P) = \int_{-\infty}^{\infty} F(\mu)\, d\mathfrak{P}_\mu = \sum_{\kappa=1}^{\infty} c_\kappa \mathfrak{P}(\delta_\kappa).$$

This definition is independent of the partition of the line. The integral has the following properties:

If $F = 0$, *then* $\int_{-\infty}^{\infty} F(\mu)\, d\mathfrak{P}_\mu = 0$. *If* $F = 1$, *the integral* $= 1$.

If $F(\mu) = a_1 F_1(\mu) + a_2 F_2(\mu)$, *then*
$$\int_{-\infty}^{\infty} F(\mu)\, d\mathfrak{P}_\mu = a_1 \int_{-\infty}^{\infty} F_1(\mu)\, d\mathfrak{P}_\mu + a_2 \int_{-\infty}^{\infty} F_2(\mu)\, d\mathfrak{P}_\mu.$$

If $F(\mu) = F_1(\mu) F_2(\mu)$, *then*
$$\int_{-\infty}^{\infty} F(\mu)\, d\mathfrak{P}_\mu = \int_{-\infty}^{\infty} F_1(\mu)\, d\mathfrak{P}_\mu \cdot \int_{-\infty}^{\infty} F_2(\mu)\, d\mathfrak{P}_\mu.$$

These properties are easy to prove if we make use of the orthogonality of the $\mathfrak{P}(\delta_\kappa)$. Note that F_1 and F_2 may have different discontinuities; in defining the integral of the product of F_1 and F_2 we should use the union of the discontinuities of F_1 and F_2 as points of partition.

If the c_κ *are complex numbers then our integral is a normal operator* (since its Hermitian components commute). *If all the* c_κ *are real, the integral is a self-adjoint operator. At all times,* $F(P)^* = \bar{F}(P)$, *where* $\bar{F}$ *is constructed by means of the* $\bar{c}_\kappa$.

As a direct consequence of our definition, we have $F(P)$ cc $\mathfrak{P}_\mu$. *For arbitrary* y *and* z *in* $\mathfrak{H}$ *we have*

$$(F(P)y, z) = \int_{-\infty}^{\infty} F(\mu)\, d(\mathfrak{P}_\mu y, z),$$

$$\|F(P)y\|^2 = \int_{-\infty}^{\infty} |F(\mu)|^2\, d\|\mathfrak{P}_\mu y\|^2.$$

We claim that both integrals above are ordinary Stieltjes integrals. In fact, the limits of integration $-\infty, \infty$ can be replaced by m and M; viewed as a function of μ, $(\mathfrak{P}_\mu y, z)$ is of bounded variation because

$$(\mathfrak{P}_\mu y, z) = \frac{1+i}{2}[(\mathfrak{P}_\mu y, y) + (\mathfrak{P}_\mu z, z)] - \frac{(\mathfrak{P}_\mu(z-y), z-y)}{2} - \frac{i}{2}(\mathfrak{P}_\mu(iz-y), iz-y)$$

and $\mathfrak{P}_\mu$ increases monotonically with μ, so that both real and imaginary parts are expressible as the difference of two monotonically increasing functions; $\|\mathfrak{P}_\mu y\|^2 = (\mathfrak{P}_\mu y, y)$ is of bounded variation because it increases monotonically with μ; moreover, from the definition of the Stieltjes integral we have

$$(F(P)y, z) = \left(\sum_{\kappa=1}^{\infty} c_\kappa \mathfrak{P}(\delta_\kappa)y, z\right) = \sum_{\kappa=1}^{\infty} c_\kappa(\mathfrak{P}(\delta_\kappa)y, z) = \int_{-\infty}^{\infty} F(\mu)\, d(\mathfrak{P}_\mu y, z).$$

A similar argument proves our second contention.

Now in order to extend our definition of integral to the case of any continuous function defined over the interval $m \leqq \mu \leqq M$, we first note that such a function is bounded and uniformly continuous over this interval and that we can take a somewhat larger interval and extend $F(\mu)$ to this larger interval in a continuous fashion.

Let us consider a sequence of partitions of our new interval by means of a finite number of subintervals $\delta_\kappa^{(n)}$ (the superscript n denotes the nth partition), in such a way that the largest subinterval of any partition tends to 0 in length as $n \to \infty$. Let us define a step function $F(\mu)$ taking on the value $F(\mu_\kappa^{(n)})$ over $\delta_\kappa^{(n)}$ at the arbitrary point $\mu_\kappa^{(n)}$ of $\delta_\kappa^{(n)}$. Then $F_n(\mu)$ tends uniformly to $F(\mu)$ as $n \to \infty$. We then form $F_n(P)$ and claim that as $n \to \infty$ this operator tends to a limit which we can designate as $F(P) = \int_{-\infty}^{\infty} F(\mu)\, d\mathfrak{P}_\mu$.

Indeed

$$\|F_n(P) - F_m(P)\| \leqq \max|F_n(\mu) - F_m(\mu)| \to 0 \quad \text{for} \quad n, m \to \infty.$$

As in the case of the ordinary integral, we can show that the above integral is independent of the sequence of partitions used and of the points $\mu_\kappa^{(n)}$.

The properties of the integral which we established in the case of step functions also hold in the general case thanks to the relation

$$\int_{-\infty}^{\infty} F(\mu)\, d\mathfrak{P}_\mu = \lim_{n\to\infty} \sum_{(\kappa)} F(\mu_\kappa^{(n)})\mathfrak{P}(\delta_\kappa^{(n)}).$$

Our definition of integral can be extended to piecewise continuous functions. All the above considerations serve to show that the integral $\int_{-\infty}^{\infty} \mu\, d\mathfrak{P}_\mu$ is well defined.

4. Spectral Representation

Let us return to the inequality (*) on p. 87, and think of it as repeatedly written for a sequence of partitions into intervals $\delta_\kappa^{(n)}$ with end points $\mu_\kappa^{(n)}$ and $\nu_\kappa^{(n)}$. If we sum all these inequalities we obtain

$$\sum \mu_\kappa^{(n)}\mathfrak{P}(\delta_\kappa^{(n)}) \leqq \mathfrak{K} \sum \mathfrak{P}(\delta_\kappa^{(n)}) \leqq \sum \nu_\kappa^{(n)}\mathfrak{P}(\delta_\kappa^{(n)}).$$

Since $\sum \mathfrak{P}(\delta_\kappa^{(n)}) = \mathfrak{I}$, and since both the sum on the right and the sum on the left tend to the same limit, we see that

$$\mathfrak{K} = \int_{-\infty}^{\infty} \mu\, d\mathfrak{P}_\mu,$$

a direct generalization of the representation of a completely continuous operator (to which it reduces by appropriate specialization).

We have therefore obtained the spectral representation of the general self-adjoint operator and shall proceed to deduce further consequences of this representation. An immediate first consequence is

$$(\mathfrak{K}y, z) = \int_{-\infty}^{\infty} \mu\, d(\mathfrak{P}_\mu y, z), \qquad \|\mathfrak{K}y\|^2 = \int_{-\infty}^{\infty} |\mu|^2\, d\|\mathfrak{P}_\mu y\|^2.$$

Another consequence, depending also on the product formula on p. 91 and on an appropriate passage to the limit, is

$$\mathfrak{K}^2 = \int_{-\infty}^{\infty} \mu^2 \, d\mathfrak{P}_\mu$$

. . . .

$$\mathfrak{K}^m = \int_{-\infty}^{\infty} \mu^m \, d\mathfrak{P}_\mu$$

for all positive integers m. By analogous procedures we can represent polynomials in $\mathfrak{K}$ and even more general functions of $\mathfrak{K}$.

Now let ξ be a real number such that $\mathfrak{P}_\mu$ is constant in a neighborhood $(\xi - \delta, \xi + \delta)$ of ξ. We shall show that ξ *does not belong to the* μ *spectrum of* $\mathfrak{K}$.

To this end we form the operator

$$\mathfrak{R}(\xi) = \int_{-\infty}^{\infty} \frac{1}{\mu - \xi} \, d\mathfrak{P}_\mu$$

by the procedure already described where we only allow partitions of the interval (m, M) containing a fixed interval around ξ in which $\mathfrak{P}_\mu$ is constant. (This interval is, of course, further subdivided.) Then for all $\mathfrak{P}(\delta_\kappa)$ which do not equal zero, our integrand is $<1/\delta$ in absolute value and continuous. Thus we can rewrite our integral in the form

$$\int_{-\infty}^{\xi-\delta} \frac{1}{\mu - \xi} \, d\mathfrak{P}_\mu + \int_{\xi+\delta}^{\infty} \frac{1}{\mu - \xi} \, d\mathfrak{P}_\mu$$

and so reduce it to two integrals of the continuous function $1/(\mu - \xi)$ taken over the intervals $(-\infty, \xi - \delta)$ and $(\xi + \delta, \infty)$. But by our previous discussion these last two integrals are well defined. We have

$$\mathfrak{R}(\xi) \cdot (\mathfrak{K} - \xi \mathfrak{I}) = \int_{-\infty}^{\infty} \frac{1}{\mu - \xi} \, d\mathfrak{P}_\mu \cdot \int_{-\infty}^{\infty} (\mu - \xi) \, d\mathfrak{P}_\mu$$

$$= \int_{-\infty}^{\infty} d\mathfrak{P}_\mu = \mathfrak{I},$$

so that at the value ξ the operator $\mathfrak{K} - \xi\mathfrak{I}$ possesses a bounded inverse, i.e., ξ does not belong to the μ spectrum of $\mathfrak{K}$, as asserted.

On the other hand, suppose ξ is a real number such that in every one of its neighborhoods we can find a couple (μ, ν) such that $\mathfrak{P}_\nu - \mathfrak{P}_\mu > 0$. Then in every neighborhood of ξ there would exist a μ_0 such that $\mathfrak{P}_\xi - \mathfrak{P}_{\mu_0} \neq 0$. We now show that *such a ξ belongs to the μ spectrum of* $\mathfrak{K}$.

Indeed, suppose that the equation $(\mathfrak{K} - \xi\mathfrak{I})y = x$ can be solved for every x in $\mathfrak{H}$. Then there must exist a uniquely determined bounded operator $\mathfrak{R}$ inverse to $\mathfrak{K} - \xi\mathfrak{I}$, in which case we could prove—as in §10.2—that there must exist a neighborhood of ξ such that for μ in this neighborhood every operator $\mathfrak{K} - \mu\mathfrak{I}$ also possesses a unique bounded inverse. In fact, the series

$$(\mathfrak{K} - \xi\mathfrak{I})^{-1}[\mathfrak{I} + (\mu - \xi)(\mathfrak{K} - \xi\mathfrak{I})^{-1} + (\mu - \xi)^2(\mathfrak{K} - \xi\mathfrak{I})^{-2} + \cdots]$$

converges for sufficiently small $|\mu - \xi|$ and the operator defined by it is

$$(\mathfrak{K} - \xi\mathfrak{I})^{-1}[\mathfrak{I} - (\mu - \xi)(\mathfrak{K} - \xi\mathfrak{I})^{-1}]^{-1} = [\mathfrak{K} - \xi\mathfrak{I} - (\mu - \xi)\mathfrak{I}]^{-1} = (\mathfrak{K} - \mu\mathfrak{I})^{-1}.$$

Certainly, then, no real μ in this neighborhood of ξ can be a spectral point of $\mathfrak{K}$. For definiteness we assume that the μ_0 above for which $\mathfrak{P}_{\mu_0} \neq \mathfrak{P}_\xi$ is $> \xi$; this involves no loss of generality.

Now we select an element y in $\mathfrak{H}$ in such a way that y belongs to $\mathfrak{M}_{\mu_0}$ but not to $\mathfrak{M}_\xi$; We can even select y to be orthogonal to all elements of $\mathfrak{M}_\xi$; this is possible because $\mathfrak{P}_{\mu_0} > \mathfrak{P}_\xi$. We then have $\mathfrak{P}_{\mu_0} y = y$ (and $(\mathfrak{P}_\xi \eta, y) = (\eta, \mathfrak{P}_\xi y) = 0$ for any η in $\mathfrak{H}$ because $\mathfrak{P}_\xi y = 0$). Hence, for $\mu < \xi$ we have

$$\mathfrak{P}_\mu y = \mathfrak{P}_\mu \mathfrak{P}_\xi y = 0.$$

Furthermore, if $\mu > \mu_0$ we have $\mathfrak{P}_\mu y = \mathfrak{P}_\mu \mathfrak{P}_{\mu_0} y = \mathfrak{P}_{\mu_0} y$. Thus in the spectral representation

$$\|\mathfrak{K}y\|^2 = \int_m^M \mu^2 \, d(\mathfrak{P}_\mu y, \mathfrak{P}_\mu y)$$

we may choose the following limits of integration:

$$\|\mathfrak{K}y\|^2 = \int_\xi^{\mu_0} \mu^2 \, d(\mathfrak{P}_\mu y, \mathfrak{P}_\mu y).$$

Similarly,

$$\|(\mathfrak{K} - \xi\mathfrak{I})y\|^2 = \int_\xi^{\mu_0} (\mu - \xi)^2 \, d\|\mathfrak{P}_\mu y\|^2.$$

Since $\|\mathfrak{P}_{\mu_0} y\|^2 \leqq \|y\|^2$, we see that $\|(\mathfrak{K} - \xi\mathfrak{I})y\|^2 \leqq |\mu_0 - \xi|^2 \cdot \|y\|^2 = \delta\|y\|^2$, where δ is arbitrarily small. On the other hand,

$$\|(\mathfrak{K} - \xi\mathfrak{I})^{-1} \cdot (\mathfrak{K} - \xi\mathfrak{I})y\|^2 = \|y\|^2$$

and, if we put $\|\mathfrak{K} - \xi\mathfrak{I}\| = A > 0$, then $\|y\|^2 \leqq A \cdot \delta\|y\|^2$ and $1 \leqq A^2\delta$. But for arbitrarily small δ this is an impossibility. This contradiction proves that ξ belongs to the μ spectrum, as asserted.

Thus, the μ spectrum can also be characterized as the totality of values μ for which in an arbitrarily small neighborhood $\nu - \mu \leqq \delta$ or $\mu - \nu \leqq \delta$ the difference $\mathfrak{P}_\nu - \mathfrak{P}_\mu \neq 0$ whenever $\nu \neq \mu$; in other words, the μ spectrum is uniquely determined by the spectral family. The μ spectrum is obviously a closed set,[7] *i.e., the limit of a sequence of values of the μ spectrum must belong to the μ spectrum.*

Apart from the values of the μ spectrum of $\mathfrak{K}$ the operator $\mathfrak{K} - \xi\mathfrak{I}$ always has a unique bounded inverse. This means that for all complex ξ and for all ξ possessing a neighborhood in which $\mathfrak{P}_\mu$ is constant, the equation $(\mathfrak{K} - \xi\mathfrak{I})y = x$ has a unique solution for all x in $\mathfrak{H}$.

The goal of this chapter—a characterization of the spectrum of an arbitrary bounded Hermitian operator by means of its spectral family—has been attained.

[7] Its complement is open. (Ed.)

§13. Spectral Theory of Bounded Normal Operators

1. Normal Operators

In the present section we propose to extend the spectral theory developed in §11 for a bounded self-adjoint operator to the case of a bounded normal operator $\mathfrak{R}$. As we know, for such a $\mathfrak{R}$ we have

$$\frac{\mathfrak{R}+\mathfrak{R}^*}{2} = \mathfrak{A}_1 = \mathfrak{A}_1{}^*, \qquad \frac{\mathfrak{R}-\mathfrak{R}^*}{2i} = \mathfrak{A}_2 = \mathfrak{A}_2{}^*,$$

$$\mathfrak{R} = \mathfrak{A}_1 + i\mathfrak{A}_2, \qquad \mathfrak{A}_1\mathfrak{A}_2 = \mathfrak{A}_2\mathfrak{A}_1.$$

Hence, by §11,

$$\mathfrak{A}_1 = \int_{-\infty}^{\infty} \mu \, d\mathfrak{P}_\mu^{(1)}, \qquad \mathfrak{A}_2 = \int_{-\infty}^{\infty} \nu \, d\mathfrak{P}_\nu^{(2)},$$

where $\mathfrak{P}_\mu^{(1)}$ and $\mathfrak{P}_\nu^{(2)}$ are the spectral families belonging to $\mathfrak{U}_1$ and $\mathfrak{A}_2$. Since $\mathfrak{P}_\mu^{(1)}$ cc $\mathfrak{A}_1$, $\mathfrak{P}_\nu^{(2)}$ cc $\mathfrak{A}_2$, and $\mathfrak{A}_1$ c $\mathfrak{A}_2$ it follows that $\mathfrak{P}_\mu^{(1)}$ c $\mathfrak{A}_2$, $\mathfrak{P}_\nu^{(2)}$ c $\mathfrak{A}_1$, and $\mathfrak{P}_\mu^{(1)}$ c $\mathfrak{P}_\nu^{(2)}$. Let us put $z = \mu + i\nu$ and

$$\mathfrak{P}_z = \mathfrak{P}_\mu^{(1)} \cdot \mathfrak{P}_\nu^{(2)}.$$

Then[8]

$$\iint_{-\infty}^{\infty} \mu \, d\mathfrak{P}_z = \int_{-\infty}^{\infty} \mu \, d\mathfrak{P}_\mu^{(1)} \cdot \int_{-\infty}^{\infty} d\mathfrak{P}_\nu^{(2)} = \mathfrak{A}_1\mathfrak{J} = \mathfrak{A}_1$$

$$\iint_{-\infty}^{\infty} \nu \, d\mathfrak{P}_z = \int_{-\infty}^{\infty} d\mathfrak{P}_\mu^{(1)} \cdot \int_{-\infty}^{\infty} \nu \, d\mathfrak{P}_\nu^{(2)} = \mathfrak{J}\mathfrak{A}_2 = \mathfrak{A}_2,$$

Hence

$$\iint_{-\infty}^{\infty} z \, d\mathfrak{P}_z = \mathfrak{A}_1 + i\mathfrak{A}_2 = \mathfrak{R}.$$

[8] Double integrals are to be defined analogously to simple integrals.

This is the spectral representation of an arbitrary bounded normal operator. Also

$$\iint_{-\infty}^{\infty} z\, d\mathfrak{P}_z = \iint_{-\infty}^{\infty} (\mu + i\nu)\, d\mathfrak{P}_\mu^{(1)}\, d\mathfrak{P}_\nu^{(2)}$$

$$= \int_{-\infty}^{\infty} \mu\, d\mathfrak{P}_\mu^{(1)} + i \int_{-\infty}^{\infty} \nu\, d\mathfrak{P}_\nu^{(2)}.$$

The spectrum of the normal operator $\mathfrak{K}$ *is composed of generally complex values* $\mu + i\nu$ *where* μ *belongs to the spectrum of* $\mathfrak{A}_1$ *and* ν *to the spectrum of* $\mathfrak{A}_2$. In every case the spectrum of $\mathfrak{K}$ lies within the square centered on the origin having $2\|\mathfrak{K}\|$ as the length of its sides, for both $\|\mathfrak{A}_1\|$ and $\|\mathfrak{A}_2\|$ are $\leqq \|\mathfrak{K}\|$. We can even claim that the spectrum lies within the circle $|z| \leqq \|\mathfrak{K}\|$, for outside this circle there is always a bounded inverse.

2. *Unitary Operators*

We shall now examine the special *case of a unitary operator* $\mathfrak{U}$ *for which we must have* $\mathfrak{U}\mathfrak{U}^* = \mathfrak{U}^*\mathfrak{U} = \mathfrak{I}$. Such an operator is always normal and we shall prove that every complex $\varrho = \mu + i\nu$ belonging to the spectrum of $\mathfrak{U}$ satisfies $|\varrho| = 1$. In fact, suppose $|\varrho| < 1$. Then the equation

$$(\mathfrak{U} - \varrho\mathfrak{I})y = x$$

possesses a unique solution for every x in $\mathfrak{H}$. This is so because the series

$$\mathfrak{I} + \varrho\mathfrak{U}^* + \varrho^2\mathfrak{U}^{*2} + \cdots$$

must converge owing to the fact that $\|\mathfrak{U}y\|^2 = (\mathfrak{U}y, \mathfrak{U}y) = (y, \mathfrak{U}^*\mathfrak{U}y) = \|y\|^2$, i.e., that $\|\mathfrak{U}\| = 1$. It follows that

$$\mathfrak{U}^*(\mathfrak{I} + \varrho\mathfrak{U}^* + \varrho^2\mathfrak{U}^{*2} + \cdots)(\mathfrak{U} - \varrho\mathfrak{I})$$

$$= \mathfrak{I} + \varrho\mathfrak{U}^* + \varrho^2\mathfrak{U}^{*2} + \cdots - \varrho\mathfrak{U}^* - \varrho^2\mathfrak{U}^* - \cdots = \mathfrak{I}.$$

When $|\varrho| > 1$, the same result holds for the series

$$-\frac{1}{\varrho}\left(\mathfrak{J} + \frac{\mathfrak{U}}{\varrho} + \frac{\mathfrak{U}^2}{\varrho^2} + \cdots\right),$$

namely,

$$-\frac{1}{\varrho}\left(\mathfrak{J} + \frac{\mathfrak{U}}{\varrho} + \frac{\mathfrak{U}^2}{\varrho^2} + \cdots\right)(\mathfrak{U} - \varrho\mathfrak{J})$$

$$= -\frac{\mathfrak{U}}{\varrho} - \frac{\mathfrak{U}^2}{\varrho^2} - \cdots + \mathfrak{J} + \frac{\mathfrak{U}}{\varrho} + \frac{\mathfrak{U}^2}{\varrho^2} + \cdots = \mathfrak{J}.$$

Hence *all spectral values of a unitary operator* $\mathfrak{U}$ *lie on the unit circle.* We can therefore put $\varrho = e^{i\varphi}$.

We shall now derive *the spectral representation of an arbitrary unitary operator* $\mathfrak{U}$.

Since $\mathfrak{U}$ is normal it admits of the spectral representation $\mathfrak{U} = \iint_{|z| \leqq 1} z\, d\mathfrak{P}_z$, the integration being over the unit disk because $\|\mathfrak{U}\| = 1$. Let us put

$$e_\varphi(z) = \begin{cases} 1 & \text{if } |z| = 1 \text{ and } 0 < \operatorname{arc} z \leqq \varphi \\ 0 & \text{otherwise} \end{cases}$$

and $\mathfrak{E}_\varphi = \iint_{|z| \leqq 1} e_\varphi(z)\, d\mathfrak{P}_z$. Since $e_\varphi{}^2(z) = e_\varphi(z)$, $e_\varphi(z) \leqq e_\psi(z)$ for $\varphi \leqq \psi$, $\lim_{\psi \to \varphi} e_\psi(z) = e_\varphi(z)$, and $e_0(z) = 0$, we see that $\mathfrak{E}_\varphi$ is a monotone family of projections continuous from the right with $\mathfrak{E}_0 = 0$. Since $e_{2\pi}(z) = \lim_{n \to \infty} |\bar{z}z|^n$, we further see that $\mathfrak{E}_{2\pi} = \lim_{n \to \infty} (\mathfrak{U}^*\mathfrak{U})^n = \mathfrak{J}$. If we put $\mathfrak{E}_\varphi = 0$ for $\varphi < 0$ and $\mathfrak{E}_\varphi = \mathfrak{J}$ for $\varphi > 2\pi$, then the spectral family $\mathfrak{E}_\varphi$ is defined for all φ. If we now assume $\varepsilon > 0$ and $0 = \varphi_0 < \varphi_1 \cdots < \varphi_n = 2\pi$, $\varphi_\kappa - \varphi_{\kappa-1} < \varepsilon$, then, for $|z| \leqq 1$, we have

$$\left| z e_{2\pi}(z) - \sum_{\kappa=1}^{n} e^{i\varphi_\kappa}(e_{\varphi_\kappa}(z) - e_{\varphi_{\kappa-1}}(z)) \right|$$

$$= \left| \sum_{\kappa=1}^{n} (z - e^{i\varphi_\kappa})(e_{\varphi_\kappa}(z) - e_{\varphi_{\kappa-1}}(z)) \right| < \varepsilon,$$

and therefore

$$\left|\mathfrak{U}\mathfrak{E}_{2\pi} - \sum_{\kappa=1}^{n} e^{i\varphi_\kappa}(\mathfrak{E}_{\varphi_\kappa} - \mathfrak{E}_{\varphi_{\kappa-1}})\right| < \varepsilon.$$

Hence

$$\mathfrak{U} = \mathfrak{U}\mathfrak{E}_{2\pi} = \int_0^{2\pi} e^{i\varphi}\, d\mathfrak{E}_\varphi.$$

§14. Unbounded Self-Adjoint Operators

1. Definitions

Up to now all the operators we have studied were defined over all of our Hilbert space $\mathfrak{H}$. We now propose to examine the case when the operator $\mathfrak{K}$ is defined only over a certain subdomain $\mathfrak{D}$ of elements of $\mathfrak{H}$. We again assume that $\mathfrak{H}' = \mathfrak{H}$, i.e., the range $\mathfrak{W}$ of values attained by $\mathfrak{K}$ is in $\mathfrak{H}$.

Since we shall again be concerned only with linear operators we assume that $\mathfrak{D}$ is a linear manifold in $\mathfrak{H}$ and that given any two elements f_1 and f_2 in $\mathfrak{D}$ we always have

$$\mathfrak{K}(c_1 f_1 + c_2 f_2) = c_1 \mathfrak{K} f_1 + c_2 \mathfrak{K} f_2.$$

Two operators will be said to be equal if they have the same domain of definition and their values are the same at each of its points.

The sum $\mathfrak{K}_1 + \mathfrak{K}_2$ of the two operators $\mathfrak{K}_1$ and $\mathfrak{K}_2$ with domains of definition $\mathfrak{D}_1$ and $\mathfrak{D}_2$ is defined over the intersection $\mathfrak{D}_1\mathfrak{D}_2$ of the two domains by the equation $(\mathfrak{K}_1 + \mathfrak{K}_2)f = \mathfrak{K}_1 f + \mathfrak{K}_2 f$, f in $\mathfrak{D}_1\mathfrak{D}_2$. Whenever $\mathfrak{K}_2 f$ belongs to $\mathfrak{D}_1$, the product $\mathfrak{K}_1\mathfrak{K}_2$ is defined by the equation $(\mathfrak{K}_1\mathfrak{K}_2)f = \mathfrak{K}_1(\mathfrak{K}_2 f)$.

If $\mathfrak{K}f = \mathfrak{K}g$ implies $f = g$, we can define the inverse operator $\mathfrak{K}^{-1}$ as follows: The domain of definition of $\mathfrak{K}^{-1}$ is the range $\mathfrak{W}$ of $\mathfrak{K}$ and $\mathfrak{K}^{-1}(\mathfrak{K}f) = f$. Thus to assure that $\mathfrak{K}^{-1}$ exists and is well defined we need only impose the condition that $\mathfrak{K}f = 0$ implies $f = 0$. Clearly, $\mathfrak{K}^{-1}$ is a linear operator.

We shall say that $\mathfrak{K}$ is *densely defined* if $\mathfrak{D}$ is dense in $\mathfrak{H}$.

We can then define the adjoint operator $\mathfrak{K}^*$ as follows: The domain of definition $\mathfrak{D}^*$ of $\mathfrak{K}^*$ is the set of those elements f in $\mathfrak{H}$ for which there exists an element f^* in $\mathfrak{H}$ such that

$$(\mathfrak{K}g, f) = (g, f^*)$$

for all g in $\mathfrak{D}$. We then define $\mathfrak{K}^*f = f^*$. The element f^* is unique, for if there were an f_1^* such that $(g, f^*) = (g, f_1^*)$, then $(g, f^* - f_1^*) = 0$ for all g in $\mathfrak{D}$. Clearly then, $\mathfrak{K}^*$ is linear. Since $\mathfrak{D}$ is dense in $\mathfrak{H}$, this would imply $f^* - f_1^* = 0$ and $f^* = f_1^*$. If $\mathfrak{D} = \mathfrak{H}$, the present definition reduces to the earlier definition of an adjoint operator.

$\mathfrak{K}$ is said to be *closed* if $f_n \to f$ and $\mathfrak{K}f_n \to h$ taken together imply that f belongs to $\mathfrak{D}$ and that $\mathfrak{K}f = h$.

As a consequence of the continuity of scalar products it follows that $\mathfrak{K}^*$ *is always closed.* For if f_n (in $\mathfrak{D}$) $\to f$ in $\mathfrak{H}$ then we must have $(\mathfrak{K}g, f_n) = (g, \mathfrak{K}^*f_n) \to (\mathfrak{K}g, f)$. If now $\mathfrak{K}^*f_n$ also converges strongly to h, we have $(g, h) = (\mathfrak{K}g, f)$ for all g in $\mathfrak{D}$, and, since $\mathfrak{D}$ is dense, $h = \mathfrak{K}^*f$, i.e., $\mathfrak{K}^*$ is closed.

A densely defined linear operator $\mathfrak{K}$ *is said to be self-adjoint if* $\mathfrak{K} = \mathfrak{K}^*$. In this case $\mathfrak{K}$, being equal to $\mathfrak{K}^*$, must also be closed. For all real λ, $\mathfrak{K} + \lambda\mathfrak{I}$ is also self-adjoint, for

$$(\mathfrak{K} + \lambda\mathfrak{I})^* = \mathfrak{K}^* + \bar{\lambda}\,\mathfrak{I} = \mathfrak{K} + \lambda\mathfrak{I}.$$

2. *Spectral Representation*

We shall now study the spectral representation of the general self-adjoint operator. With this in mind, let us first note the identity

$$\begin{aligned} \|\mathfrak{K}f + if\|^2 &= (\mathfrak{K}f, \mathfrak{K}f) + i(f, \mathfrak{K}f) - i(\mathfrak{K}f, f) + (f, f) \\ &= \|\mathfrak{K}f\|^2 + \|f\|^2. \end{aligned}$$

This identity shows that if $\mathfrak{K}f + if = 0$, then $f = 0$ and consequently $(\mathfrak{K} + i\mathfrak{I})^{-1}$ must exist. The domain of this operator is the set of all elements $(\mathfrak{K} + i\mathfrak{I})f$, ($f$ in $\mathfrak{D}$), while its range is the set of all f. If we put $\mathfrak{U} = (\mathfrak{K} - i\mathfrak{I})(\mathfrak{K} + i\mathfrak{I})^{-1}$, then the domain of definition of $\mathfrak{U}$ is the set of all elements $(\mathfrak{K} + i\mathfrak{I})f$.

We now show that the domain of definition of $\mathfrak{U}$ is dense in $\mathfrak{H}$. In fact, if h is orthogonal to $(\mathfrak{R} + i\mathfrak{I})f$, then $((\mathfrak{R} + i\mathfrak{I})f, h) = 0$, i.e.,

$$(\mathfrak{R}f, h) = -(if, h) = (f, ih).$$

This means that h belongs to the domain of definition of the adjoint of $\mathfrak{R}$ and we must have

$$ih = \mathfrak{R}^*h = \mathfrak{R}h$$

$$(\mathfrak{R} - i\mathfrak{I})h = 0, \qquad \text{hence} \quad h = 0.$$

Therefore all the values $(\mathfrak{R} + i\mathfrak{I})f$ (f in $\mathfrak{D}$) are dense in $\mathfrak{H}$, as asserted. The values of $\mathfrak{U}$ are $(\mathfrak{R} - i\mathfrak{I})f$ (f in $\mathfrak{D}$).

From $g = (\mathfrak{R} + i\mathfrak{I})f$ and $\mathfrak{U}g = (\mathfrak{R} - i\mathfrak{I})f$ it follows that $\frac{1}{2}(g - \mathfrak{U}g) = if$ and $\frac{1}{2}(g + \mathfrak{U}g) = \mathfrak{R}f$. If $g - \mathfrak{U}g = 0$, then $g + \mathfrak{U}g = 0$ and hence $g = 0$. This assures the existence of $(\mathfrak{I} - \mathfrak{U})^{-1}$. We have $g = 2i(\mathfrak{I} - \mathfrak{U})^{-1}f$ and therefore

$$\mathfrak{R}f = \tfrac{1}{2}(\mathfrak{I} + \mathfrak{U})g = i(\mathfrak{I} + \mathfrak{U})(\mathfrak{I} - \mathfrak{U})^{-1}f.$$

Since $\mathfrak{D}$ is equal to the range of $\mathfrak{I} - \mathfrak{U}$, the latter must be dense in $\mathfrak{H}$.

Since $g = (\mathfrak{R} + i\mathfrak{I})f$ and $\mathfrak{U}g = (\mathfrak{R} - i\mathfrak{I})f$, it follows that $\|\mathfrak{U}g\|^2 = \|g\|^2$ and $\|\mathfrak{U}g\| = \|g\|$, and hence, if g and h belong to the domain of definition of $\mathfrak{U}$, $(\mathfrak{U}g, \mathfrak{U}h) = (g, h)$; this is because

$$\left\|\frac{x+y}{2}\right\|^2 - \left\|\frac{x-y}{2}\right\|^2 + i\left\|\frac{x+iy}{2}\right\|^2 - i\left\|\frac{x-iy}{2}\right\|^2 = (x, y)$$

for x, y in $\mathfrak{H}$. This implies that $\mathfrak{U}^*$ is defined for all $f = \mathfrak{U}h$ and that $h = \mathfrak{U}^*f$. Hence $\mathfrak{U}^*\mathfrak{U}h = h$ for all h in the domain of definition of $\mathfrak{U}$, i.e., for all $h = (\mathfrak{R} + i\mathfrak{I})y$ (y in $\mathfrak{D}$). Since the set of such h's is dense in $\mathfrak{H}$, we always have $\mathfrak{U}^*\mathfrak{U} = \mathfrak{I}$; likewise, $\mathfrak{U}\mathfrak{U}^* = \mathfrak{I}$. Thus, $\mathfrak{U}$ *is unitary* and bounded and so admits the representation

$$\mathfrak{U} = \int_0^{2\pi} e^{i\varphi}\, d\mathfrak{E}_\varphi.$$

$\mathfrak{D}$ consists of all elements of the form $g = (\mathfrak{I} - \mathfrak{U})h$ (h in $\mathfrak{H}$). For such a g we have

$$\|\mathfrak{E}_\varphi g\|^2 = \|\mathfrak{E}_\varphi(\mathfrak{I} - \mathfrak{U})h\|^2 = \|(\mathfrak{I} - \mathfrak{U})\mathfrak{E}_\varphi h\|^2$$
$$= \int_0^{2\pi} |1 - e^{i\psi}|^2 \, d\|\mathfrak{E}_\psi \mathfrak{E}_\varphi h\|^2 = \int_0^{\varphi+0} |1 - e^{i\psi}|^2 \, d\|\mathfrak{E}_\psi h\|^2$$
$$= \int_0^{\varphi+0} 4 \sin^2 \frac{\psi}{2} \, d\|\mathfrak{E}_\psi h\|^2.$$

Hence

$$(*) \qquad \int_0^{2\pi} \cot^2 \frac{\varphi}{2} \, d\|\mathfrak{E}_\varphi g\|^2 = \int_0^{2\pi} \cot^2 \frac{\varphi}{2} \, 4 \sin^2 \frac{\varphi}{2} \, d\|\mathfrak{E}_\varphi h\|^2$$
$$= 4 \int_0^{2\pi} \cos^2 \frac{\varphi}{2} \, d\|\mathfrak{E}_\varphi h\|^2.$$

This integral is therefore convergent, and hence the projection $\mathfrak{E}_\varphi g$ can have no jump discontinuity for $\varphi = 2\pi$. Since the elements g are dense in $\mathfrak{H}$, every function $\mathfrak{E}_\varphi f$ (f in $\mathfrak{H}$) is continuous for $\varphi = 2\pi$. Since these functions are also continuous for $\varphi = 0$, the integral

$$H = \int_0^{2\pi} \left(-\cot \frac{\varphi}{2}\right) d\mathfrak{E}_\varphi$$

exists and is a self-adjoint operator. In view of $(*)$ the domain of definition of this operator is all of $\mathfrak{D}$. Moreover,

$$(Hg, g) = \int_0^{2\pi} \left(-\cot \frac{\varphi}{2}\right) d\|\mathfrak{E}_\varphi g\|^2$$
$$= \int_0^{2\pi} \left(-\cot \frac{\varphi}{2}\right) 4 \sin^2 \frac{\varphi}{2} \, d\|\mathfrak{E}_\varphi h\|^2$$
$$= \int_0^{2\pi} i(1 + e^{i\varphi})(1 - e^{-i\varphi}) \, d\|\mathfrak{E}_\varphi h\|^2$$
$$= i((\mathfrak{I} + \mathfrak{U})(\mathfrak{I} - \mathfrak{U}^*)h, h)$$
$$= (i(\mathfrak{I} + \mathfrak{U})h, (\mathfrak{I} - \mathfrak{U})h) = (\mathfrak{K}g, g),$$

which implies that $Hg = \mathfrak{R}g$ for every g in $\mathfrak{D}$.[9] Hence $H = \mathfrak{R}$ and thus

$$\mathfrak{R} = \int_0^{2\pi} \left(-\cot\frac{\varphi}{2}\right) d\mathfrak{E}_\varphi = \int_{-\infty}^{\infty} \mu \, d\mathfrak{P}_\mu$$

with $\mu = -\cot(\varphi/2)$ and $\mathfrak{P}_\mu = \mathfrak{E}_{-2 \operatorname{arc\,cot} \mu}$. *This is the spectral representation of* $\mathfrak{R}$.

3. Semibounded Operators

A special case that merits attention is that of the semibounded self-adjoint operator $\mathfrak{R}$. By definition, such an operator is characterized by the existence of a fixed real number c such that $(\mathfrak{R}y, y) \geqq c(y, y)$. Then $\mathfrak{R}_1 = \mathfrak{R} - (c-1)\mathfrak{I}$ has the property that

$$(\mathfrak{R}_1 y, y) = ((\mathfrak{R} - (c-1)\mathfrak{I})y, y) \geqq (y, y).$$

Hence $\mathfrak{R}_1 y = 0$ implies that $(\mathfrak{R}_1 y, y) = (y, y) = 0$, i.e., $y = 0$ and thus $\mathfrak{R}_1^{-1}$ exists, is defined everywhere, and bounded—for $z = \mathfrak{R}_1 y$ is dense for y in $\mathfrak{D}$,[10] $\mathfrak{R}_1^{-1}(\mathfrak{R}_1 y) = y$ implies $(\mathfrak{R}_1^{-1}(\mathfrak{R}_1 y), y) = (y, y) \leqq (\mathfrak{R}_1 y, y)$, i.e., $(\mathfrak{R}_1^{-1} z, y) \leqq (z, y)$, so that $(\mathfrak{R}_1^{-1} z, \mathfrak{R}_1^{-1} z) \leqq (z, \mathfrak{R}_1^{-1} z) \leqq (z, z)$. On the other hand,

$$\begin{aligned}(\mathfrak{R}_1^{-1} z, z) &= (\mathfrak{R}_1^{-1} z, \mathfrak{R}_1 y) = (\mathfrak{R}_1(\mathfrak{R}_1^{-1} z), y) \\ &= (\mathfrak{R}_1 y, y) \geqq (y, y) \geqq 0.\end{aligned}$$

Hence $\mathfrak{R}_1^{-1}$ is positive and bounded, $0 \leqq \mathfrak{R}_1^{-1} \leqq \mathfrak{I}$. Let us put $\mathfrak{R}_1^{-1} = \int_0^1 \lambda \, d\mathfrak{O}_\lambda$, where $\mathfrak{O}_\lambda$ denotes the associated spectral family. From

$$\int_0^1 \frac{1}{\lambda} \, d\mathfrak{O}_\lambda \cdot \int_0^1 \lambda \, d\mathfrak{O}_\lambda = \int_0^1 1 \cdot d\mathfrak{O}_\lambda = \mathfrak{I}$$

[9] Cf. footnote on p. 83. (Ed.)

[10] Let $h \perp$ range of $\mathfrak{R}_1$. Then $(\mathfrak{R}_1 y, h) = 0$. Let $y_n \to h$. Then $0 = (\mathfrak{R}_1 y_n, h) = (y_n, \mathfrak{R}_1^* h) = (h, \mathfrak{R}_1^* h) = (\mathfrak{R}_1 h, h)$; hence $h = 0$. This implies that the range of $\mathfrak{R}_1$ is dense. (Ed.)

we deduce that $\mathfrak{K}_1 = \int_0^1 (1/\lambda)\, d\mathfrak{D}_\lambda$. Consequently

$$\mathfrak{K} = \int_0^1 \left(\frac{1}{\lambda} + c - 1\right) d\mathfrak{D}_\lambda = \int_c^\infty \mu\, d\mathfrak{P}_\mu,$$

where $\mu = (1/\lambda) + c - 1$, $\lambda = 1/(\mu - c + 1)$ and $\mathfrak{P}_\mu = \mathfrak{J} - \mathfrak{D}_{(\mu-c+1)^{-1}-0}$. We have thus obtained the spectral representation in a new and simple way. At the same time, we see that if the semibounded transformation possesses the greatest lower bound c, then $\mathfrak{P}_\mu = 0$ for $\mu < c$.

§15. Examples and Applications

1. The set of all real harmonic functions defined over a domain $\mathfrak{G}$ (functions such that $\Delta u = 0$ over $\mathfrak{G}$) furnishes us with an example of a Hilbert space. These functions obviously form a linear space $\mathfrak{H}$, so that axiom (a) is satisfied. We define the scalar product of two harmonic functions u and v by means of the integral

$$(u, v) = \iint_{\mathfrak{G}} u(x, y)v(x, y)\, dx\, dy.$$

This means that we must limit ourselves to those harmonic functions u for which $\iint_{\mathfrak{G}} u^2\, dx\, dy$ is finite. Naturally, we shall only allow real numbers to be our scalars. Hence, the norm of u is given by

$$\|u\|^2 = \iint_{\mathfrak{G}} u^2(x, y)\, dx\, dy$$

and it likewise fulfills the necessary requirements. To verify axiom (c) *we must show that a Cauchy sequence of harmonic functions $u_1, u_2, \cdots$ i.e., a sequence for which*

$$\|u_n - u_m\|^2 = \iint_{\mathfrak{G}} (u_n - u_m)^2\, dx\, dy \to 0 \qquad \text{as} \quad n, m \to \infty$$

converges to a limit function which is also harmonic in $\mathfrak{G}$.

In order to prove this, we first establish:

(1) *Every Cauchy sequence of harmonic functions converges pointwise*, and even uniformly, over any closed subset contained in the interior of $\mathfrak{G}$ *to a (continuous) limit function* $u(x, y)$.

To prove this lemma, consider the well-known mean value integral for harmonic functions,

$$u(P) = u(x, y) = \frac{1}{2\pi}\int_0^{2\pi} u(Q)\, d\varphi,$$

where Q varies over the boundary of a circle of radius r centered on P and contained in $\mathfrak{G}$. By a second integration, this time with respect to r, between the limits 0 and R we get the following representation:

$$u(P) = \frac{1}{\pi R^2}\iint_K u(Q)\, dx\, dy.$$

By means of Schwarz's inequality, we now can see that

$$|u_m(P) - u_n(P)| = \left|\frac{1}{\pi R^2}\iint_K (u_m(Q) - u_n(Q))\, dx\, dy\right|$$

$$\leq \frac{1}{\pi R^2}\sqrt{\pi R^2 \cdot \iint_K |u_m(Q) - u_n(Q)|^2\, dx\, dy}$$

$$\leq \frac{1}{R\sqrt{\pi}}\sqrt{\iint_{\mathfrak{G}} |u_m(Q) - u_n(Q)|^2\, dx\, dy} \to 0.$$

Since this inequality holds uniformly for all points belonging to a closed subset of $\mathfrak{G}$, the asserted existence of a continuous function $u(P)$, P an interior point of $\mathfrak{G}$, follows.

(2) *We shall now examine the partial derivatives* $\partial u_n/\partial x$ *and shall prove that over every subdomain* $\mathfrak{G}'$ *lying in the interior of* $\mathfrak{G}$ *these derivatives themselves form a Cauchy sequence.* Let us put $u_n - u_m = v$ and then consider a function H, defined equal to 1 in the interior of the boundary curve $\mathfrak{C}'$ of $\mathfrak{G}'$ ($\mathfrak{C}'$ lies completely in the interior of $\mathfrak{G}$) and decreasing smoothly

to 0 in the annular domain bounded by $\mathfrak{C}'$ and $\mathfrak{C}$, the boundary curve of $\mathfrak{G}$. Then

$$\iint_{\mathfrak{G}} v_x^2 H\,dx\,dy \leqq \iint_{\mathfrak{G}} (v_x^2 + v_y^2) H\,dx\,dy$$

$$= -\iint_{\mathfrak{G}} v[v_{xx}H + v_x H_x + v_{yy}H + v_y H_y]\,dx\,dy,$$[11]

and since $\Delta v = 0$, we also have

$$-\iint_{\mathfrak{G}} v[v_x H_x + v_y H_y]\,dx\,dy = \frac{1}{2}\iint_{\mathfrak{G}} (v^2 H_{xx} + v^2 H_{yy})\,dx\,dy$$

$$\leqq M \iint_{\mathfrak{G}} v^2\,dx\,dy$$

$$= M \cdot \|u_n - u_m\|^2.$$[12]

Here M is the maximum of $|H_{xx}|$ and $|H_{yy}|$ in $\mathfrak{G}$. Since the right side above tends to 0 as $m, n \to \infty$, the same must hold for the left side, which tells us that

$$\iint_{\mathfrak{G}} H\left(\frac{\partial u_n}{\partial x} - \frac{\partial u_m}{\partial x}\right)^2 dx\,dy \to 0,$$

[11] Here use is made of Green's theorem:

$$\iint_{\mathfrak{G}} \left(\frac{\partial Q}{\partial x} - \frac{\partial P}{\partial y}\right) dx\,dy = \int_{\mathfrak{C}} P\,dx + Q\,dy,$$

where $\mathfrak{C}$ bounds $\mathfrak{G}$. Specifically,

$$vx^2 H = \frac{\partial}{\partial x}(v \cdot v_x H) - v \cdot \frac{\partial}{\partial x}(v_x H) = \frac{\partial}{\partial x}(v \cdot v_x H) - v(v_{xx}H + v_x H).$$

Similarly, $vy^2 H = (\partial/\partial y)(v \cdot v_y H) - v(v_{yy}H + v_y H)$. Now apply Green's theorem with $Q = v(v_x H)$ and $P = -v(v_y H)$ bearing in mind that H vanishes on $\mathfrak{C}$. (Ed.)

[12] Here Green's theorem is used with $P = \frac{1}{2}v^2 H_x$, $Q = -\frac{1}{2}v^2 H_y$. P and Q vanish on $\mathfrak{C}$ because H goes smoothly to zero, that is, H_x and H_y vanish on $\mathfrak{C}$. (Ed.)

i.e.

$$\iint_{\mathfrak{G}'} \left(\frac{\partial u_n}{\partial x} - \frac{\partial u_m}{\partial x}\right)^2 dx\, dy \to 0$$

over all domains $\mathfrak{G}'$ lying in the interior of $\mathfrak{G}$.

This implies that the $\partial u_n/\partial x$ form a Cauchy sequence in $\mathfrak{G}'$. Since each $\partial u_n/\partial x$ is a harmonic function, we see (by 1. above) that, within every $\mathfrak{G}'$, $\partial u_n/\partial x$ converges pointwise to a limit function continuous in $\mathfrak{G}$. Similarly, $\partial u_n/\partial y$ is a Cauchy sequence of harmonic functions and as such converges pointwise to a continuous function in $\mathfrak{G}$. Hence the same conclusion holds for all derivatives of the u_n. It remains to prove:

(3) *The limits of the derivatives are the appropriate derivatives of the limit function* $u(x, y)$. This result is an immediate consequence of the uniform convergence of the sequence of the derivatives. These considerations imply that $\lim_{n\to\infty} \Delta u_n = \Delta u = 0$, which proves that axiom (c) is verified.

As for axiom (d), we must demonstrate the existence of a denumerable fundamental set in $\mathfrak{H}$. We already know that the $\mathfrak{L}^2$-integrable functions of two variables defined over the whole plane constitute a Hilbert space $\mathfrak{L}_2$ and hence this space possesses a denumerable fundamental set. Now, the space of functions harmonic in $\mathfrak{G}$ constitutes a subspace of $\mathfrak{L}_2$ and hence, by the later results of §3, this subspace must also possess a fundamental set which is at most denumerably infinite. On the other hand, it is easy to find a denumerably infinite number of linearly independent elements in $\mathfrak{H}$ (e.g., polynomials); therefore the dimension of $\mathfrak{H}$ is denumerably infinite.

If, instead of using the previously given definition of scalar product for the space $\mathfrak{H}$ of harmonic functions, we employ the definition

$$(u, v) = \iint_{\mathfrak{G}} \operatorname{grad} u \cdot \operatorname{grad} v \, dx\, dy,$$

we obtain a new space of harmonic functions—the space of those harmonic u for which $\iint_{\mathfrak{G}} (\operatorname{grad} u)^2\, dx\, dy$ is finite. *We propose to prove that this new space is also a Hilbert space.* First, axiom (a) obviously still holds. Axiom (b) presents some difficulties, for if $\|u\| = 0$ it does not follow that $u = 0$ but only that $u =$ constant.

We can obviate this difficulty by considering only those functions $u(P)$ which vanish at a certain fixed inner point P_0; this removes the freedom of our arbitrary constant, and then $\|u\| = 0$ implies $u(P) = \text{constant} = u(P_0) = 0$. Thus axioms (a) and (b) hold. As for axiom (c), if we consider a Cauchy sequence u_n for which $\|u_n - u_m\| \to 0$ as $n, m \to \infty$, then the harmonic functions $\partial u_n/\partial x$ form a Cauchy sequence in the previously defined norm, for we have

$$\iint_{\mathfrak{G}'} \left(\frac{\partial u_n}{\partial x} - \frac{\partial u_m}{\partial x}\right)^2 dx\, dy \leqq \iint_{\mathfrak{G}} (\text{grad}(u_n - u_m))^2\, dx\, dy \to 0.$$

Hence there exists in $\mathfrak{G}$ a harmonic limit function $v = \lim_{n\to\infty} (\partial u_n/\partial x)$. The same holds for the Cauchy sequence $\partial u_n/\partial y$ whose limit is a harmonic function w. Furthermore, we evidently have $\partial v/\partial y = \partial w/\partial x$. If we now put

$$u = \int_{P_0}^{P} v\, dx + w\, dy,$$

then u is independent of the path of integration (in the interior of $\mathfrak{G}$), and we have

$$\frac{\partial u}{\partial x} = v, \qquad \frac{\partial u}{\partial y} = w,$$

which implies that $\lim_{n\to\infty} u_n = u$ is an element of our space $\mathfrak{H}$. Indeed, if $\Delta u_n = 0$ then $\Delta u = 0$, and $\iint_{\mathfrak{G}} (\text{grad}\, u)^2\, dx\, dy$, being the limit of $\iint_{\mathfrak{G}} (\text{grad}\, u_n)^2\, dx\, dy$, must be finite (by Fatou's theorem[13]). The validity of axiom (d) follows from essentially the same considerations as in the previous case.

[13] Séries trigonométriques et séries de Taylor, *Acta Math.* **30** (1906), 335–400.

2. Let $f(z) = \sum_{n=-\infty}^{\infty} a_n z^n$ be a Laurent series, convergent in the ring $\varrho \leqq |z| \leqq R$, where $0 < \varrho < 1 < R$. Let us form the "all-sided" $\mathfrak{L}$ matrix

$$\begin{pmatrix} \cdots & & & & & & & & \\ \cdots & a_{-2} & a_{-1} & a_0 & a_1 & a_2 & \cdots & & \\ & \cdots & a_{-2} & a_{-1} & \boxed{a_0} & a_1 & a_2 & \cdots & \\ & & \cdots & a_{-2} & a_{-1} & a_0 & a_1 & a_2 & \cdots \\ & & & \cdots & & & & & \end{pmatrix}$$

which represents a bounded operator in the Hilbert space of sequences $(\cdots x_{-2}, x_{-1}, x_0, x_1, x_2, \cdots)$. The reader should prove this contention and also that the product of two such Laurent series corresponds to the product of their associated $\mathfrak{L}$ matrices which is itself an $\mathfrak{L}$ matrix. The reader may now try to show that the spectrum of an $\mathfrak{L}$ matrix consists of the values attained by $f(z)$ when $|z| = 1$. If $a_{-n} = \bar{a}_n$, then this spectrum is real and the operator in question is self-adjoint. Using the substitution $z = e^{i\varphi}$ we can represent the values of $f(z)$ on the unit circle by means of the Fourier series

$$a_0 + 2\sum_{n=1}^{\infty} (a_n \cos n\varphi - \beta_n \sin n\varphi) \qquad (a_n = \alpha_n + i\beta_n).$$

These values are all nonnegative if and only if the associated Hermitian $\mathfrak{L}$ form is positive, i.e., when all the principal minors of this $\mathfrak{L}$ form are $\geqq 0$. Hence, the conditions which guarantee that the above Fourier series takes on only values $\geqq 0$ are $a_0 \geqq 0$, $a_0^2 - |a_1|^2 \geqq 0$, and, in general,

$$\begin{vmatrix} a_0 & a_1 & \cdots & a_{n-1} \\ \bar{a}_1 & a_0 & a_1 & \cdots & a_{n-2} \\ \cdots\cdots & \cdots\cdots & \cdots\cdots & \cdots \\ \bar{a}_{n-1} & \bar{a}_{n-2} & \cdots & a_0 \end{vmatrix} \geqq 0.$$

The derivation of these conditions seems to imply that they hold only for those Fourier series which represent analytic functions which can be analytically continued beyond their interval of periodicity. But these conditions also hold in other cases, such as in the case of uniformly convergent, hence continuous, Fourier series defined over $-\pi \leqq \varphi \leqq \pi$ with $y(\pi) = y(-\pi)$. We leave the proofs of these contentions to the reader. (Cf. O. Toeplitz, Theorie der $\mathfrak{L}$-Formen, *Math. Ann.* **70**, (1911), 351–376.

Many investigations in the theory of crystal lattices reduce to the problem of the free vibrations of the lattice. In order to determine them we must set up the equations of motion for a particle of the lattice due to the forces exerted by the remaining particles. Thus, let an elementary cell of the lattice contain s particles and let this cell be extended by repeated translations in the direction of three vectors $\mathfrak{a}_1, \mathfrak{a}_2, \mathfrak{a}_3$. We designate by $\mathfrak{K}_{kk'}^{ll'}$ the force exerted by the particle (k', l') on the particle (k, l); here (k, l) designates the kth particle $(k = 1, 2, \cdots, s)$ having mass m_k and lying within the cell $l = (l_1, l_2, l_3)$ defined by the translation $l_1\mathfrak{a}_1 + l_2\mathfrak{a}_2 + l_3\mathfrak{a}_3$ (l_1, l_2, l_3 integers). The equation of motion for the displacement $\mathfrak{u}_k^l$ associated with the particle (k, l) now reads

$$m_k \ddot{\mathfrak{u}}_k^l = \sum_{k'l'} \mathfrak{K}_{kk'}^{ll'} = \mathfrak{K}_k^l.$$

The summation is to be carried out over all (k', l') distinct from (k, l). In order to calculate the forces we shall make use of the potential between the two points (k, l) and (k', l') which we designate by $\varphi_{kk'}^{l-l'} = \varphi_{kk'}|(\mathfrak{r}_k^l - \mathfrak{r}_{k'}^{l'}|)$. Here $\mathfrak{r}_k^l$ stands for the position vector of the particle (k, l). This potential depends only upon the distance of the two points.

If we now introduce the displacement $\mathfrak{u}_k^l$ and examine the total potential G, expanded in powers of the change in displacement $\mathfrak{u}_k^l - \mathfrak{u}_{k'}^{l'}$, we obtain the following expression:

$$G = \sum_{k'l'} \varphi_{kk'}^{ll'} = \sum_{k'l'} \left[\varphi_{kk'}^{l-l'} + \frac{\partial}{\partial x} \varphi_{kk'}^{l-l'} \cdot (\mathfrak{u}_k^l - \mathfrak{u}_{k'}^{l'})_x + \cdots \right.$$

$$\left. + \frac{1}{2}\left(\frac{\partial^2}{\partial x^2} \varphi_{kk'}^{l-l'} \cdot (\mathfrak{u}_k^l - \mathfrak{u}_{k'}^{l'})_x^2 + \cdots \right) + \cdots \right].$$

Here $(u_k^l - u_{k'}^{l'})_x$ are the x components of the change in displacement, etc.

The force applied to one particle because of the existence of all the other particles is

$$\mathfrak{K}^l_{kx} = -\frac{\partial G}{\partial \mathfrak{u}^l_{kx}}$$

$$= -\sum_{k'l'} \frac{\partial \varphi^{l-l'}_{kk'}}{\partial x} - \sum_{k'l'} \frac{\partial^2}{\partial x^2} \varphi^{l-l'}_{kk'}(\mathfrak{u}^l_k - \mathfrak{u}^{l'}_{k'})_x - \cdots .$$

In our case, that of vibration about a point of equilibrium, the first sum to the right of this equation must be equal to 0; limiting ourselves to terms of the first degree, we get

$$\mathfrak{K}^l_{kx} = -\sum_{k'l'} \left[\frac{\partial^2}{\partial x^2} \varphi^{l-l'}_{kk'}(\mathfrak{u}^l_k - \mathfrak{u}^{l'}_{k'})_x + \frac{\partial^2}{\partial x \partial y} \varphi^{l-l'}_{kk'}(\mathfrak{u}^l_k - \mathfrak{u}^{l'}_{k'})_y \right.$$

$$\left. + \frac{\partial^2}{\partial x \partial z} \varphi^{l-l'}_{kk'}(\mathfrak{u}^l_k - \mathfrak{u}^{l'}_{k'})_z \right]$$

$$= \sum_{k'l'} \left[\frac{\partial^2}{\partial x^2} (\varphi^{l-l'}_{kk'})\mathfrak{u}^{l'}_{k'x} + \frac{\partial^2}{\partial x \partial y} (\varphi^{l-l'}_{kk'})\mathfrak{u}^{l'}_{k'y} + \frac{\partial^2}{\partial x \partial z} (\varphi^{l-l'}_{kk'})\mathfrak{u}^{l'}_{k'z} \right],$$

for if all $\mathfrak{u}^{l'}_{k'} = 0$, then the force on the particle (k, l) must be zero.

Substituting this expression in the equations of motion and introducing the plane wave

$$\mathfrak{u}^l_k = \mathfrak{x}_k e^{i(l(\varphi) - \omega t)}, \qquad l(\varphi) = l_1\varphi_1 + l_2\varphi_2 + l_3\varphi_3$$

we get

$$m_k \omega^2 \mathfrak{x}_{kx} + \sum_{k'l'} \left[\frac{\partial^2}{\partial x^2} (\varphi^{l-l'}_{kk'})\mathfrak{x}_{k'x} + \frac{\partial^2}{\partial x \partial y} (\varphi^{l-l'}_{kk'})\mathfrak{x}_{k'y} \right.$$

$$\left. + \frac{\partial^2}{\partial x \partial z} (\varphi^{l-l'}_{kk'})\mathfrak{x}_{k'z} \right] e^{i(l'(\varphi) - l(\varphi))} = 0$$

and two other similar equations for $\mathfrak{x}_{ky}$, $\mathfrak{x}_{kz}$. For fixed l_1, l_2, l_3 and a definite choice of $\varphi_1, \varphi_2, \varphi_3$ we therefore have a system of $3s$ equations in the $3s$ unknowns $\mathfrak{x}_{kx}, \mathfrak{x}_{ky}, \mathfrak{x}_{kz}$. But this system must be independent of the choice of l_1, l_2, l_3 since no cell has been singled out; hence, there is no loss in generality in putting $l_1 = l_2 = l_3 = 0$.

Of necessity, the determinant of order $3s$ associated with this system must vanish; this furnishes $3s$ values for ω^2, which by their very definition must be positive. Once we have these values we can calculate up to a proportionality factor the associated vectors $\mathfrak{x}_k$, i.e., the amplitudes and phases of the vibrations within a cell. This is true for every choice of $\varphi_1, \varphi_2, \varphi_3$, which we can assume to be restricted to $-\pi \leqq \varphi \leqq \pi$.

The reader should clearly perceive the analogy between the above considerations and the previously developed theory of $\mathfrak{L}$ matrices. In fact, in the crystal lattice problem we are really employing a generalized $\mathfrak{L}$ matrix whose elements $a_{l-l'}$ depend only upon the difference between the indices l and l', where these indices run through a three-dimensional lattice and the elements themselves stand for $3s$-fold matrices. In reducing the problem of frequency determination to a determinant equation of order $3s$, we were really showing that the spectrum of the operator associated with the $\mathfrak{L}$ matrix is determined by the roots of the characteristic equation of degree $3s$ in ω^2.

Our theory holds provided a certain convergence condition holds. In the case of simple $\mathfrak{L}$ matrices, this condition is equivalent to the regularity of the Laurent series in the neighborhood of the unit circle. Putting $l - l' = \nu$, this means that the $6s^2$ functions

$$\sum_{(\nu)} \frac{\partial^2}{\partial x^2} (\varphi_{kk'}^{\nu}) z_1^{\nu_1} z_2^{\nu_2} z_3^{\nu_3},$$

$$\sum_{(\nu)} \frac{\partial^2}{\partial x \partial y} (\varphi_{kk'}^{\nu}) z_1^{\nu_1} z_2^{\nu_2} z_3^{\nu_3},$$

$$\cdots$$

$$\sum_{(\nu)} \frac{\partial^2}{\partial z^2} (\varphi_{kk'}^{\nu}) z_1^{\nu_1} z_2^{\nu_2} z_3^{\nu_3}$$

are analytic in z_1, z_2, z_3 and regular in the neighborhood of the unit circles $|z_1| = 1$, $|z_2| = 1$, $|z_3| = 1$. Also, note that for every system of values $\varphi_1, \varphi_2, \varphi_3$ with $|\varphi_\alpha| \leqq \pi$, the "continuous spectrum" of the operator furnishes a solution of the homogeneous equations which is represented by the vector $\mathfrak{x}_k (k = 1, \cdots, s)$ or, equivalently, its $3s$ components. Note that this vector (and its infinitude of iterations) is not a vector in the associated Hilbert space because the sum of the absolute values of the squares of its components does not converge. This corresponds to the fact that a point μ belonging to the interval spectrum need not be a vector solution of the homogeneous operator equation. These vector solutions to the homogeneous operator equation come from points μ of the point spectrum (eigenvalues) and only in special cases are these μ also points of the continuous spectrum. (Cf. "Enzyklopaedie d. math. Wissenschaften," Vol. 3; M. Born, "Dynamik der Kristallgitter," pp. 527–781, in particular No. 18; "Handbuch der Physik," XXIV. 2; M. Born and M. Goeppert-Mayer, "Dynamische Gittertheorie der Kristalle," pp. 623–794, in particular No. 12 Cf. also Zur Theorie der "p-fach-zyklischen" Matrizen der Ordnung n in the author's "Vortraege ueber Determinanten und Matrizen," Berlin, 1949, especially p. 29 and following (if we let $n \to \infty$, this class of matrices goes over into the class of generalized $\mathfrak{L}$ matrices).

3. *Let $\mathfrak{K}$ be a self-adjoint operator, μ_0 a point in its μ spectrum, and suppose μ_0 is the only point of the spectrum lying in the interval (α, β). Let $y \neq 0$ in $\mathfrak{H}$ and put*

$$\eta = \frac{(\mathfrak{K}y, y)}{\|y\|^2}, \qquad \varepsilon = \frac{\|\mathfrak{K}y - \eta y\|}{\|y\|}.$$

We shall call y an approximate eigenvector associated with the approximate eigenvalue η $(\alpha \leqq \eta \leqq \beta)$. Then

$$\eta - \frac{\varepsilon^2}{\beta - \eta} \leqq \mu_0 \leqq \eta + \frac{\varepsilon^2}{\eta - \alpha}$$

and this relation yields better bounds on the eigenvalue only if $\varepsilon^2 < (\eta - \alpha)(\beta - \eta)$.[14]

[14] What is asserted is that if $\varepsilon^2 < (\eta - \alpha)(\beta - \eta)$, then we can enlarge the interval in which μ_0 is the only eigenvalue, that is, $\eta - \varepsilon^2/(\beta - \eta) < \alpha$ and $\eta + \varepsilon^2/(\eta - \alpha) > \beta$. (Ed.)

Without loss of generality we may assume that $\eta = 0$ and $\|y\| = 1$.[15] From the spectral representation of $\mathfrak{K}$ we have

$$(\mathfrak{K}y, y) = \int_{-\infty}^{\infty} \mu \, d(\mathfrak{P}_\mu y, y).$$

If we put $(\mathfrak{P}_\mu y, y) = \varrho(\mu)$, then $\int_{-\infty}^{\infty} \mu \, d\varrho = \eta = 0$, and furthermore $\int_{-\infty}^{\infty} d\varrho = 1$ and $\int_{-\infty}^{\infty} \mu^2 \, d\varrho = (\mathfrak{K}^2 y, y) = (\mathfrak{K}y, \mathfrak{K}y) = \varepsilon^2$. Now $\varrho(\mu)$ has only one point of discontinuity μ_0 in the interval (α, β). The function $(\mu - \mu_0)(\mu - \beta)$ represents a parabola passing through the points μ_0 and β of the μ axis and is therefore positive outside the interval (μ_0, β). Hence

$$0 \leqq \int_{-\infty}^{+\infty} (\mu - \mu_0)(\mu - \beta) \, d\varrho = \varepsilon^2 + \mu_0 \beta,$$

which implies that $\mu_0 \geqq -\varepsilon^2/\beta$. This proves our first contention. The second contention follows from an analogous argument using the function $(\mu - \mu_0)(\mu - \alpha)$.

A particular case of interest occurs when $\alpha = -\infty$. Then our operator is without eigenvalues to the left of μ_0, hence semibounded, with μ_0 the first eigenvalue (it can occur with multiplicity greater than one). We then have Temple's theorem:

$$\eta - \frac{\varepsilon^2}{\beta - \eta} \leqq \mu_0 \leqq \eta.$$

4. In classical mechanics, the energy of a system with f degrees of freedom can be given by a function of the generalized real coordinates $q_1, \cdots, q_f$ and their derivatives with respect to time $\dot{q}_1, \cdots, \dot{q}_f$:

$$T(q_1, \cdots, q_f, \dot{q}_1, \cdots, \dot{q}_f) + V(q_1, \cdots, q_f),$$

where T stands for kinetic energy, V for potential energy. If we eliminate the $\dot{q}_1, \cdots, \dot{q}_f$ by means of the generalized momenta

$$p_k = \partial \mathfrak{L} / \partial \dot{q}_k \, (k = 1, \cdots, f)$$

(where $\mathfrak{L}(\dot{q}_k, q_k) = T(q_k, \dot{q}_k) - V(q_k)$ is the Langrangian of

[15] Otherwise we replace $\mathfrak{K}$ by $\mathfrak{K} - \eta\mathfrak{J}$ and y with $y/\|y\|$. (Ed.)

Newtonian mechanics) we obtain

$$H = \sum_{k=1}^{f} \dot{q}_k p_k - \mathfrak{L}(\dot{q}_k, q_k) = H(q_k, p_k)$$

or the Hamiltonian, which, if it does not explicitly contain the time variable t, must represent the total energy of the system and hence must be important for studying extrema and stationary values of the energy.

In quantum mechanics, in place of the variables $q_1, \cdots, q_f$, $p_1, \cdots, p_f$ we have operators $\mathfrak{Q}_1, \cdots, \mathfrak{Q}_f$, $\mathfrak{P}_1, \cdots, \mathfrak{P}_f$ in the Hilbert space of $\mathfrak{L}_2$-integrable functions y of $q_1, \cdots, q_f$, with the usual definition of norm, and

$$\mathfrak{Q}_k y = q_k y, \qquad \mathfrak{P}_k y = \frac{h}{2\pi i} \frac{\partial y}{\partial q_k} \qquad (k = 1, \cdots, f).$$

(Here h denotes Planck's constant.) These operators are connected by the relations

$$\left.\begin{aligned} \mathfrak{Q}_\alpha \mathfrak{Q}_\beta - \mathfrak{Q}_\beta \mathfrak{Q}_\alpha &= 0 \\ \mathfrak{P}_\alpha \mathfrak{Q}_\beta - \mathfrak{Q}_\alpha \mathfrak{P}_\beta &= \frac{h}{2\pi i} \delta_{\alpha\beta} \\ \mathfrak{P}_\alpha \mathfrak{P}_\beta - \mathfrak{P}_\beta \mathfrak{P}_\alpha &= 0 \end{aligned}\right\} \qquad (\alpha, \beta = 1, \cdots, f).$$

The operators are self-adjoint by definition.

Since for y in $\mathfrak{L}_2$ the derivative $\partial y / \partial q_k$ need not exist and belong to $\mathfrak{L}_2$ and since for y in $\mathfrak{L}_2$, $q_\alpha y$ need not belong to $\mathfrak{L}_2$, it follows that the operators are defined in a part of $\mathfrak{H}$ and are therefore not bounded. The same is true of the operator $H = H(\mathfrak{Q}_1, \cdots, \mathfrak{Q}_f, \mathfrak{P}_1, \cdots, \mathfrak{P}_f)$, which can be written in various ways owing to the relations connecting the $\mathfrak{P}_\alpha$ and the $\mathfrak{Q}_\beta$. H is a self-adjoint operator and therefore the spectral theory of this chapter applies to it.

We consider the example of the hydrogen atom where we are interested in the relative motion of its single electron about the nucleus which is regarded as the origin of the coordinate system. Here $f = 3$; q_1, q_2, q_3 are the three position coordinates of the electron and the energy can be written in the form

$$H(q_1 q_2 q_3 p_1 p_2 p_3) = \frac{1}{2m}(p_1^2 + p_2^2 + p_3^2) + V(q_1 q_2 q_3).$$

The first term on the right represents the kinetic energy and the second term, the potential energy. By Coulomb's law $V = -e^2/r$ $(r = \sqrt{q_1^2 + q_2^2 + q_3^2}$, $e =$ charge). Introduction of the corresponding operators yields the quantum-mechanical relation

$$H = H(\mathfrak{Q}_1 \mathfrak{Q}_2 \mathfrak{Q}_3 \mathfrak{P}_1 \mathfrak{P}_2 \mathfrak{P}_3)$$

$$= \frac{1}{2m}(\mathfrak{P}_1^2 + \mathfrak{P}_2^2 + \mathfrak{P}_3^2) - e^2 \sqrt{\mathfrak{Q}_1^2 + \mathfrak{Q}_2^2 + \mathfrak{Q}_3^2}^{\,-1},$$

and this, applied to the function y, which must be twice differentiable, means that

$$H = -\frac{h^2}{8m\pi^2}\Delta y - \frac{e^2}{r}y.$$

In order to determine the spectral representation of this self-adjoint operator we must first examine the solutions of the equation

$$Hy = \mu y$$

for real μ. On introducing polar coordinates r, ϑ, φ this equation (Schroedinger's equation) can be reduced (as usual, using Bernoulli's lemma) to a set of subsidiary equations, each of which contains only one of the variables r, ϑ, φ.

In the case of negative energy the calculations lead to a denumerable infinity of values μ_α, the stationary values of the energy, while for the associated eigenfunctions, the calculations lead to expressions involving Laguerre functions in r and trigonometric functions in ϑ and φ which together constitute a complete orthonormal system in $\mathfrak{H}$.

This means that, with the assumptions we have made above, we are led to a pure point spectrum and hence the spectral representation of our operator can be explicitly determined. We leave it to the reader to carry out the calculations in detail.

It is well worth noting that, according to the statistical formulation of atomic theory, the square of the absolute value of each eigenfunction (which we can assume to have been normalized in $\mathfrak{H}$) multiplied by the appropriate element of volume can be interpreted as the probability that the electron can be found in that volume element during an infinitesimal stretch of time.

BIBLIOGRAPHY

I. Fundamental papers

FREDHOLM, I.

Sur une classe d'équations fonctionnelles, *Acta Math.* **27** (1903), 365–390.

Les équations intégrales linéaires, *C. R. Stockholm* (1910), 92–100.

HILBERT, D.

"Grundzüge einer allgemeinen Theorie der linearen Integralgleichungen." Leipzig, 1912.

TOEPLITZ, O. and HELLINGER, E.

Integralgleichungen und Gleichungen mit unendlich vielen Unbekannten. "Enc. d. Math.," II, C, 13. Leipzig, 1927.

SCHMIDT, E.

Zur Theorie der linearen und nichtlinearen Integralgleichungen, *Math. Ann.* **63** (1907), 433–476; **64** (1907), 161–174.

RIESZ, F.

"Les systèmes d'équations linéaires a une infinité d'inconnues." Paris, 1913.

v. NEUMANN, J.

Allgemeine Eigenwerttheorie Hermitescher Funktionaloperatoren, *Math. Ann.* **102** (1930), 49–131.

Zur Algebra der Funktionaloperatoren und Theorie der normalen Operatoren, *Math. Ann.* **102** (1930), 370–427.

II. Monographs

v. SZ. NAGY, B.

"Spektraltheorie linearer Transformationen des Hilbertschen Raumes." Berlin, 1942.

STONE, M. H.

"Linear transformations in Hilbert Space and Their Applications to Analysis." Amer. Math. Soc., New York, 1932 (Coll. Publ. vol. XV).

BANACH, S.

"Théorie des opérations linéaires." New York, 1952.

WINTNER, E.

"Spektraltheorie der unendlichen Matrizen." Leipzig, 1929.

v. NEUMANN, J.

"Mathematical Foundations of Quantum Mechanics." Princeton, 1955.

"Functional operators." Princeton, 1950.

RIESZ-NAGY

"Functional Analysis." New York, 1955.

HALMOS
"Introduction to Hilbert space and the theory of Spectral Multiplicity." New York, 1951.
v. MISES, R.
"Wahrscheinlichkeitsrechnung und ihre Anwendung in der Statistik und theoretischen Physik." New York, 1945.
AKHIEZER, N. I., and GLAZMAN, I. M.
"Theory of Linear Operators in Hilbert Space." New York, 1961 (Vol. I); 1963 (Vol. II).
TAYLOR, A. E.
"Introduction to Functional Analysis." New York, 1958.
ZAANEN, A. C.
"Linear Analysis." Groningen, 1956.
DUNFORD, N., and SCHWARTZ, J. T.
"Linear Operators." New York, 1958 (Part I. General theory); 1963 (Part II. Spectral theory. Self-adjoint operators in Hilbert Space); In preparation. (Part III. Spectral operators).

SUBJECT INDEX